C000179285

Love, Hate and Armour-Plated Handbags

A Cautionary Tale Based On True Life Events
By Clare Walker

© Copyright Clare Walker 2020. All rights reserved.

The right of Clare Walker to be identified as the author of this work has been asserted by her in accordance with the Copyright, Designs and Patents Act, 1988.

This story is a based on true life events and, while some characters are real, in some instances names have been changed in order to protect their identity. Additionally, other characters, although inspired by real people, have been fictionalised for the purposes of this work and are not intended to represent any actual persons living or dead.

All views and comments printed in this book are those of the author and should not be attributed to the publisher.

I want you to know that I heard it all, every word. Nothing went unnoticed, unappreciated or unloved. I heard it all, dear Evelynne, so I wrote this book for you

Contents

Starry, Starry Night

I saw a shooting star.

It blazed past the little window of my grandparents' bedroom in the early hours of the morning, lighting up the sky.

I was sitting on a yellow plastic potty, pulled from under their bed, having a wee, my vest and Bri-Nylon nightie tucked firmly under my armpits, as was usual in order to prevent a dip. After all, no one wants urine on their bedwear, unless of course the party's going particularly well.

I leant on the over-washed and somewhat faded pink and green candlewick bedspread which covered the bed, my sore eyes stinging with every blink, a pain inflicted from fat tears cried earlier that night.

Shooting star had woken me from a dozy state. It sped past so fast and bright and then … nothing; the sky, without its glow, black once more.

I was left staring back into an empty sky, eyes like saucers, cold in the dark room, the only sound now from my grandmother's deep-sleep breathing and Granddad's snoring – which was loud.

Evelynne, my grandmother, had always been a salt-over-the-shoulder, superstitious kind of person. She told me that shooting stars, like blue flames, black cats and being shat on by pigeons, were symbolic of good luck, and being a gravitator to the positive pole myself, I was inclined to agree.

I shivered, stood up, and with some care pushed the potty back. Then, tucking my nightie between my legs, steadily mounted the bed, squeezing myself tightly between the the soft, warm, slumbering bodies – safely back in the bunker.

The three-in-a-bed thing wasn't meant to be a regular occurrence. It was, however, my first place of refuge whenever the shit hit the fan, and to be honest, during this period of my life, shit tended to hit fans on a regular basis – tons of it, quite frankly; tons of dark brown shit, splattering huge oscillating fans.

My own bed was, in fact, located in the room across the hall.

Well, I say my own bed: I was in a bed-share with my sister Frances who was two years older than me – nice girl but, as it turned out, no head for strategic warfare, which was something that was definitely going to be required if either of us was going to live to see the Diddy Men strike a new marmalade seam, watch the next cliffhanging episode of *The Herb Garden* or paint Kitty Clarke's face red, ever again.

I, on the other hand, had developed quite a good nose for a ruck; a sort of inflammatory response, if you will, to the first and significant signs of danger. It is no exaggeration to say that by the time I was six years old, I had become quite a slick troubleshooter, with the acquired ability to get into the lifeboat before anyone else had even noticed the ship was sinking.

I was born in Sheffield, in 1963 – the Year of the Cat – and my name is Clare.

Love, Hate and Armour-Plated Handbags

Sheffield, like most northern cities, was built on heavy industry and strong women. The mining and textile industries provided the livelihood for millions of northern families, but in Sheffield, steel was king.

Located on the banks of the River Don, Sheffield soon became the world's steel capital which, during the Industrial Revolution, brought thousands of working-class families to settle from all over the country and, in the late 1950s, more from further afield, such as Ireland, India, Pakistan, Poland, the West Indies and the Caribbean Basin; all settled around the steelworks, located predominantly in Attercliffe and Pitsmoor.

In 1957, Bill Hinchliffe was glad he lived in Pitsmoor. Like him, it was swinging: a real cosmopolitan melting pot of music, colour, culture and creed. He was twenty-two years old, very tall, very dark and incredibly handsome. He wore tailored suits and smoked cigarettes. His skin tanned easily with minimum exposure to the sun, and his chiselled face was accentuated by china-blue eyes and a very strong but perfectly proportioned nose, which gave him an air of Sinatra.

Bill had always been a bit of an athlete. He played football for Sheffield United and Burnley, and during National Service had been the captain of the RAF football team. He loved cricket, opera and poetry, read Shakespeare, could speak Russian and drank gin and tonic. He was, in short, the very essence of suavity, and always felt outwith his working-class environment.

That said, his politics were firmly rooted in the Labour Party – he was a socialist. After leaving the RAF, Bill had taken up some casual work to support his on–off football career. Although football was his first love, it didn't really pay well, and certainly wasn't going to subsidise his passion for Senior Service and bespoke tailoring. Further, he had no desire to work in the smelting shop at Tempered Springs like his father, on twelve-hour shifts, wearing dreadful navy overalls, waiting for retirement, a gold watch and a Teasmade. That did not appeal to him at all. No, he was going to take his own sweet time and think about it, but for now the job working for Fletcher's suited him. Okay, driving round

Sheffield in a bread van, selling fondant fancies and teacakes, wasn't exactly the height of glamour, but it was easy money and he enjoyed the attention he got from the young girls, who, since his appointment, had developed a sudden interest in popping out for a family sliced, armed with their padded bras and Max Factor lipstick.

Still, and as tantalising as all *that* was, in reality, Bill was only living for the weekend, and to him, half-day Friday was a much more important reason for staying with the cakes, because in this 1950s northern England, Friday night was club night, whether you were a member of the Irish Club, the Labour Club, the Conservative Club (not many takers there), that cool Afro-Caribbean Club or a cross-fertilisation of all. Yes, indeed, Friday night was massive and the early dart a gift – the chance of a lunchtime snifter, a couple of hours nappage and a quick wash and brush-up, before hitting the anti-social social club and busting a move into town for the dance.

***

Leaning on the bar at a late-night Locarno, Bill stood and watched – he didn't do dancing; dancing, like heavy manual labour, wasn't really his thing – as the band swung in and out on its revolving stage, from saxophone to guitar, from 'Young Love' to 'Green Door', the room was beginning to swell with Julie London lookie-likies, cigarette smoke and the odd group of Teddy boys, their Brylcreemed hair combed into elephant trunks and bad versions of Bobby Darin.

'Why do they do it?' he whispered, draining his glass and turning inward to order another.

Barman had seen him. 'Wi, you soon, mate.' He pointed to Bill's glass. 'Same agen?'

'Please,' replied Bill. He didn't use the word 'mate'; it wasn't part of his lexicon and, apart from that, he was sure that James Mason or Dirk Bogarde had never called anyone 'mate' either.

'On second thoughts,' he said, 'make it a double.' And with that, felt the sudden sharp jab of a finger, right in the middle of his back. Okay. He'd been here before, so, shoving his wallet back into its pocket, slowly turned, first to the left and then to the right, until he felt a tap on his shoulder and, circling back round, was indeed smacked, and smacked hard – punched in the face by an eyeful of exquisite.

She was incredible: crimson lips, blue eyes, jet-black bouffant hair, perfectly curled and elegantly coiffed. Impeccably styled and flawlessly groomed – what a doll!

'I can't get served,' she shouted over the music, pressing a shilling into his hand. 'Can you get me a Babycham?'

'No, that's alright.' He said, quick to push the money back. 'I'll get you this.'

'Really? Well, thank you, kind sir.'

Now, being more than slightly fickle, Bill couldn't decide if the 'kind sir' was a put off or not. He wasn't sure if he'd been left feeling slightly cold – was she thick?

He shook his head. Don't think about it, maybe it was just a slip. He resigned himself to letting it go. He'd go back over it when he got home, break it down verbatim and then decide if her beauty could at all outstrip the ridiculous and, quite frankly, embarrassing comment.

His instincts were half right. Stella Beatrice Gunn hadn't exactly set the heather alight, having left school at the age of fifteen without a single qualification. Despite this handicap, she was every inch the beauty, and tonight her perfect body was elegantly framed in a white lace dress, falling mid-calf and cinched at the waist by a black satin sash, matched to black satin heels, setting off her slim ankles to perfection. Bill liked girls with small feet and slim ankles. The three-quarter-length sleeves exposed tiny wrists and milky white skin. *Good skin*, he thought, handing her the Babycham.

That night they'd chatted into the early hours. Bill walked her home, even giving her a piggyback ride after her shoes had cut into her heels like knives.

'You'll never get the bloodstains out of these,' he said later, leaning against the lamp post outside her front gate, holding them up to the light.

'Who cares? It's not as if I'll be wearing them again.'

'Suppose not,' he said, handing back the shoes. 'Far too painful.'

Stella shot him a puzzled look. 'No, it's not that,' she laughed. 'Can't be seen in the same pair twice. What would people say?'

Bill was sure that people wouldn't even notice, much less say anything.

'Ah, you and Princess Margaret, eh?'

'That's right,' she said. 'Me and Princess Margaret.'

But Princess Margaret doesn't live on the Manor and work at SR Gents sewing gussets into girdles. Is she for real?

Yep, he'd definitely need a rewind at some stage, but for now, back to that face, perfectly lit as it was, in the subtle glow of streetlight. She really did have great skin and, it had to be said, the cutest little snout he thought he'd ever seen: so cute, that he was more than prepared to put the 'kind sir' and the 'Princess Margaret' thing to one side, and take her out again.

'D'you want to meet again sometime?' he asked, half scared of the rejection.

'Alright, why not? Lunchtime? Or evening? What were you thinking?'

'Erm, Friday night maybe?'

'Friday?' She smiled, masking the disappointment. A whole week? He's happy to wait a whole bloody week? And what's with the *maybe*? Was there something wrong with him?

He hadn't even tried to kiss her, which was odd, very odd indeed. 'Okay,' she continued, 'Friday night it is. Pick me up here, at say … seven-ish?'

'Okey-dokey. See you next Friday.' He leant in and kissed her head, pausing for just a second or two before finally letting her go.

Stella frowned. 'Right, bye then,' and, feeling more than slightly patronised, made her way up the crazy paving, fumbling for her key.

'Yeah, bye then.' It had started to rain as he pulled the lapels of his Barney Goodman jacket tightly to his chest.

Walking home gave Bill time to reflect. Okay, she's no Barbara Castle, but then again, who is? And with a face like that, does she really need a brain? And, and, and, she was quite funny in her own way. Good genes, seriously good genes. He knew Friday would be an opportunity to check the parents out, before committing to anything like a second date. He'd best make sure her looks weren't just a fluke, and the rest of the family hadn't been whacked by the ugly stick, or she'd got some spack-faced brother lurking in the background.

After all, Bill had taken on a certain identity, people saw him in a certain way; he had to be well reflected.

While clearly matched in the looks department, Stella and Bill were not matched in the fundamentals of intellect, humour or taste, and Bill's one and only objective, as far as this relationship was concerned, was to breed, preferably mini versions of his own narcissistic self. From set-off he had no real interest in Stella, what made her happy, what made her sad, what made her laugh, what made her cry. He saw her as good genetic material and nothing else. The mother of his children would have to be a looker – he was quite misogynistic like that.

Then again, this *was* the nineteen-fifties and choice didn't exactly feature on the dance card. He knew he was an imposter, but not intentionally so; mute and void, he couldn't really love anyone, never mind someone as flimsy as her, and in a funny sort of way, that's what made her so perfect.

Stella, on the other hand, knew Bill thought himself superior, but enjoyed the trophy boyfriend. He impressed everyone he met with his looks, his style, his intelligence. She really liked that; it turned her on, and so she duly dangled him on her arm like a 1957 'It' bag, much to the dismay of her friends. Yep, there was definitely a brain in that hair. Stella was divisive by nature and would always be able to outmanoeuvre him when it came to getting what she wanted. What she lacked in intellect, she certainly made up for in power politics, so when she became pregnant just a few weeks later, Bill decided to seal fate and propose. He bought a recording of Frank Sinatra singing the Cole Porter classic 'You're Sensational' and wrote a poem she was to read after listening to the song.

At eighteen years old, her stomach expanding by the day and falling face down into a combination of horseshit and surface charm, Stella said 'Yes' to Bill's proposal, and my parents were married.

In 1958 their 'love child' was born: a pretty blonde girl named Elizabeth.

Stella suffered the indignity of forceps and stitches during the birth, which shot her body to hell. She sat on a rubber ring for days on end, crying and cradling her baby, listening to the irritating commands of the fat nurse who insisted she, 'Get the baby to latch on to the nipple, dear.'

'I can't. 'She won't suck. She cries and screams and scratches at me,' snapped Stella.

'Stop being such a silly girl. Hold her head and direct the breast firmly to her mouth. It really is very simple. Why you girls make such a fuss, I just don't know.'

'She's got thrush in her mouth,' cried Stella, 'an' I feel like mi tits have been run over by a train!'

'Come, come. Try again. Hold her head and guide her on.'

'Are you deaf? I've just told you, I-can't-fucking-well-do-it! So why don't you just piss off, and go and do something a bit more constructive instead – like combing your friggin back!'

The nurse shook her head as she took the baby from Stella, who in turn collapsed into her pillow crying hysterically.

'I'll speak to Sister. We'll get something for the tenderness and make up some formula so baby doesn't suffer.' She shot Stella a disapproving look, which was wasted.

Stella stayed face down in despair, lamenting her life; the life she'd had before the stretch marks, fanny-stitching, sleep deprivation and sore tits, which were the size of barrage balloons and getting bigger by the hour. During her pregnancy she'd missed her tight-fitting dresses, her high-heeled shoes, and the effect she had on men as she walked on by. But most of all, she missed the dance, the build-up to a night out, the smoky hall and the noise from her friends as they competed to be heard over the music. *The music, the music* … It was then that the gaping hole of reality finally dawned: rock around the clock; tick tock, tick tock, tick tock.

'I'm eighteen years old,' she whined, crying silently into her sleep.

***

Meanwhile, safely back on his four-moon planet and, melting the magma on a three-day bender at that all-embracing hotspot of entertainment, the Corner Pin, Bill had taken a break from work in order to congratulate himself on his latest achievement: a gorgeous baby girl, not a club foot, lazy eye or cleft palate in sight, just pure baby perfection.

'Mission accomplished,' he smugged, sinking the last of his gin and tonic and staggering back to the bar for a refill.

Staring into an empty glass, his thoughts now turned to that of his young bride. What was wrong with her? Why couldn't she see the honour bestowed upon her? Why was she so content to let standards slip? Her breasts had grown completely out of control and, quite frankly, scared him more than the mood swings. *Why does she have to be so difficult? Her language is appalling ... Really, appalling.*

***

The next three years were spent juggling work, the Corner Pin and the baby ... in that order.

Arguments became a daily occurrence as the relationship between husband and wife became more and more turbulent. Bill knew his indifference was the root cause of his wife's unhappiness, but had no desire whatsoever to even attempt to give her the attention she craved. Sex was tolerated: he didn't want her in that way, and only gave in now and again to shut her up.

So when she became pregnant with their second child, Stella thought that this would be the perfect opportunity to fix the problems in their marriage. But alas, and perhaps predictably, it was nothing of the sort.

Frances was born in 1961. She was the facsimile of her father – black hair, blue eyes; the polar opposite of her sister, but just as perfect.

This time Stella was determined to snap back into shape. She'd learnt from baby number one that wallowing in self-pity wasn't going to win her the attention of her husband. In fact, it was more likely to drive the vain, spineless, self-obsessed bastard further away. No, Stella needed a plan. The well-fitted, fictitious fabric of *his* life hadn't changed, but hers was unrecognisable. She'd been in labour longer than Harold Wilson, and the breastfeeding, nappy-scrubbing misery of isolation had finally turned this petulant, happy-go-lucky, boil-in-the-bag party girl into a flat and depressed postnatal husband-hater.

'If you think I'm staying here with kids swinging off mi tits twenty-four hours a day, you're wrong,' she spat.

'Fine, I'll get my mother to look after them.'

'Why don't you take a turn for a change? See what it's like being up to your elbows in shit an' sick!'

Bill glared at her. She looked like some sort of potato-picking peasant: her hair was scraped off her face and held in place by a cheap plastic slide; she wasn't wearing make-up or stockings; and her dress tugged around the baby bump, that she, in his opinion, had never quite got rid of.

'Like I said, I'll speak to my mother. And meantime, maybe you could have a discussion with yourself.' He ran a pointed finger up and down her body. 'The badly-stuffed-sofa look is a bit of a disappointment.'

Stella flew at him, but he caught her fist and held it tight. 'Tut-tut, Stella, you'll have to be a bit quicker than that,' he snarled.

'And you'll have to be a bit less deluded if you think I don't know what you're about! After all, it wasn't my brain I left on the labour bench.'

He shoved her back.

But Stella wasn't finished. 'Don't get me wrong,' she biled. '*I'm* not interested in your sordid little affair, but I doubt your mother will be so keen on babysitting when *she* finds out, and I can only imagine the look on your father's stupid face!'

Bill lunged at her, grabbing her by the throat, his grip getting tighter and tighter.

'I ... I ... ca- I ...' She couldn't get her words out. This was it: he was going choke the life out of her. She looked into eyes mean and narrow and full of hatred, as the thrill of panic shot through her veins. She hadn't pushed his button like this for years and was beginning to feel strangely aroused by the triumph of it all.

But Bill was frozen, his hands wrapped tightly around her neck, until suddenly he jolted into a grim realisation of what was actually happening. Then, eyes wide open, he released his grip and let her go.

Stella fell against the sink, breathing hard and deep. Her rasping shocked him, as he stumbled out into the cold dark street.

With his wife crying over the kitchen sink, Bill turned to take one more look. He wasn't disappointed. Not at all. To be disappointed you'd have to care. And Bill didn't care about his wife. He really didn't care at all.

***

Badly-Stuffed-Sofa Gate had been a flashpoint for Stella, a catalyst for turning the starvathon up to full power. She'd been nil by mouth for days and had made herself violently sick during a ludicrously obsessive exercise regime, in an attempt to tighten up her lower body and get her figure back on track. So when she discovered she was pregnant for a third time, it was the worst possible situation she could have contemplated.

'The lying bastard!'

'Sorry?' quizzed Doctor Weir, staring at her over his black-framed glasses.

'He's fucked me over for the very last time!' She drew her coat from the back of the chair and rose to leave.

'Mrs Hinchliffe,' said the doctor, 'are you alright?'

Stella turned her incredulous stare to meet him, unable to grasp why the fuck he couldn't understand the bomb he'd just dropped – like a big brown bucket of shit all over her shampoo and set.

'Alright? Am I *alright*?' Her voice rising with anger.

'Funnily enough, no I'm not. I'm twenty-three years old, with a third bloodsucking parasite on the way, married to a prancing alcoholic who genuinely believes that *the Arts* hold the key to world peace, and has more than just a casual interest in Montgomery Clift! So why, in the name of Liz Taylor's left tit, would I be alright?'

Doctor Weir was used to such abuse. His surgery on Burngreave Road had nursed many a potty mouth through a difficult time so, unshaken, he continued. 'A child, Mrs Hinchliffe, is a blessing and I'm sure – no, more than sure – that when your hormones have levelled off and you feel baby growing deep inside you, you will be content and looking forward to the delivery of a healthy happy child.'

Stella glared at him. Shall I pull those glasses off his big bald

15

head and ram them down his supercilious throat, or whack him bang square between his peevish little eyes, twat him out? She really was minded to do it, and do it bloody well, but in a moment had thought better of it, so, leaning inwards, smiled sweetly and with a soft slow retort, whispered, 'Switch off, you plank of wood,' before exiting the surgery, leaving the door wide open behind her.

***

'Ah, good timing. Tea's just mashed,' chirped Delice, as Stella scuttled backwards through the kitchen door, closing her umbrella and shaking it into the drizzling rain still falling outside.

She moved towards her best friend, planting a kiss on her cheek. 'Don't know if I can stomach it,' she said. 'I'm right off tea and coffee since I got caught up the creek without a paddle.' She pointed to her stomach. 'Or a canoe, for that matter!' Then, opening her red woollen coat, took her place at the table, folding her black silk headscarf neatly onto the back of the chair.

'Poor you,' soothed Delice. 'Poor bloody you.' She sat down. 'Well,' she said, lighting up a Park Drive, 'might be time to de-shit the creek, then.'

Stella squeezed a knackered smile. '"De-shit the creek?" What does *that* mean?'

'Well, let's face it. You don't want this kid, an' Bill would never let you get rid of it – well not in the conventional way, that is – so we may have to give it a push … if you, erm … get my drift?'

'Oh yeah? How? I'm not getting involved in any knitting-needle, crochet-hook shit, an' don't say throw myself down the frigging stairs. I might break my bloody face and that would *really* upset me!'

'I'm not suggesting you leave any visible evidence. Bloody hell, *no*! He'd never forgive you for that one. He wouldn't even let you take those morning sickness tablets the doctor gave you last incubation day.' She paused. 'Mind you, he did have a bit of a point there, I suppose.'

'Suppose,' said Stella, feeling queasy from the tea.

'No,' continued Delice, 'the method I'm proposing will not only deal with the issue in hand, but also give you the added bonus of a miscarriage sympathy card and, who knows, y'might even squeeze a new coat out of the selfish twat by way of compensation.'

Stella looked at her friend: ever wise and always together, the very blonde and not-so-dumb Delice, living in her perfect two-up two-down on Pye Bank Road with her handsome husband, Terry, a security guard at Woolworths, and her two-year-old son, Sherwin, sat on the floor playing with his police car, oblivious to their plotting.

'Manufacture a miscarriage? How?' Still sipping, nervously.

'Hot baths, gin, fags, starvation, star jumps – at least two hundred a day,' ordered Delice, with a nod to the belly. 'That ought to flush the little fucker out.'

Stella thought about it. It was true, she wasn't looking like a mother in the first bloom of pregnancy. Even her own mother had commented on how pale and thin she was, encouraging her to go to the doctor.

'I'm not sure,' she said. 'It's no one's fault but my own. I'm the one making all the mess.'

'Look,' snipped Delice, 'I know how easy it is to get lost in the shuffle, but it's *not* your fault. He's walking all over you, an' you've really got to put a stop to it, put your bloody hoof down for a change.'

'That's just it: I'm not sure I can. I haven't got the energy. I'm sick an' I'm tired, tired of all the lies, the hate, the bile-spewing fights, all of it, it's wearing me down, I can't do it. I just can't. Not any more.' Then, head in hands, unsettled and unnerved by the jeopardy that engulfed her, Stella began to weep.

'Yes you can, Stella. It's easy. Just give up giving in for a change.'

'It might be easy from where you're sitting, but there are things you don't know; stuff you wouldn't understand.'

'Try me.'

Silence.

'Come on, try me.'

Stella paused, as the tears continued to flow. This was getting difficult and difficult needed an explanation. 'I hate it,' she whispered. 'Being pregnant … it's the devil's work. But when I'm pregnant, he's kind. He shows a different side, and I think he can change, that I can change him, but then I can't, and the more he pulls away, the more I try to claw him back. An' on an' on, an' on it goes, till we're right back where we started and I'm worth my weight in baby again.'

Realising the directness of her tone, Delice came to embrace her friend. 'Don't do it, Stel. Don't let him wear you down an' rag you out like this. You're a film star, not a bloody baby machine, twanking about scrubbing the floors and washing the bloody nappies. It's no life – really, no life, not when there's no love.'

'Love?'

'Yes, Stella, love … imagine that.'

Stella shook her head.

'Seriously, you've got to put a stop to it, before it really does get too bloody late.'

But it was too late. Stella was exhausted, life weighed heavy and she'd been left empty-handed. It was hard for her to love; love had been her great disappointment, her lesson and ultimately, her downfall.

They sat for a moment in gentle acknowledgement of the predicament she faced, until Stella finally decided to give up on the tea.

'Well,' she said, 'I imagine it's just like fire. Too close you burn: too remote, you freeze.'

'What is?' asked Delice.

'Love,' she whispered. 'Love.'

And Sherwin started to cry.

***

And so it was that Stella became hooked on fags, gin and strenuous exercise. However, despite her tenacity nothing had worked, and seven months into her pregnancy she gave birth to a premature baby girl, who was immediately rushed into incubation and put on life support.

Bill was raging. 'Look what she's done this time! The death wish she's put on my little girl is now surely going to kill her! The bitch! The self-centred, attention-seeking bitch!'

He walked at speed to the bed where his wife lay, her face turned into the pillow, blank in expression.

'Happy now? Got what you wanted?'

No response.

'D'you really hate me that much, that you'd do this?'

She turned her body towards him. '*You?* I haven't done anything to you! You did it to yourself. You swore you hadn't come inside me. You lied and now you can live with it.'

Bill shook his head, slow and deliberate as if to pronounce his disgust; the warm rancid odour of hospital was making him nauseous. 'You'll pay for this,' he said. 'We both will.' Then, turning his back, set off and out of the ward.

But Stella wasn't having that. She sat bolt up and with a sudden gush of venom cried: 'Well you never know your luck, she might just do us a favour and die! Then we'll all be off the fuckin' hook, won't we?'

Bill stopped dead in his tracks. He felt the rage crack down his spine, his neck prickling with heat and hatred, his fists clenched into fight mode.

Biting his lower lip, his body started to shake with pure adrenalin. He could feel the warm trickle of blood sliding down his chin, the queasy smell of iron and the sense of being out of control. He stared at the doors ahead of him. He could quite happily turn around right now and smash her face to a pulp with the vase of flowers her simpering bitch of a mother had bought her – bludgeon her to death, or throttle the life out of her, looking into her eyes as she panicked and gasped, feeling the relief as she expired her very last breath.

This image flashed through his head with such lightning speed, it almost floored him.

'Like I said,' he whispered, 'you'll pay this.' And, pushing back his hair, continued through the double doors to his baby girl instead.

Later that night, he left the hospital without returning to see his wife. He felt too bad, too distraught and moreover, too guilty. He'd have to go back home, break the news to his parents, mask the facts and cushion the blow. He didn't want them to know that the injuries to his little girl hadn't really been caused by his wife's lack of care for herself or that of her unborn child, but by his own inability to demonstrate a sense of responsibility to himself or those around him. He'd been denying what was going on for far too long. This was payback, and he knew he'd have to take his share of this dreadful blame.

Although deep in his heart he knew his parents would never openly blame him, Evelynne, his mother, would worry herself sick, and William, his father, would wear an expression of quiet disappointment – the one that always made Bill feel small, insecure and quite frankly like the twat he was.

***

At a pre-op meeting some two weeks later, the doctor was attempting to explain things like survival rates, mortality, risks and procedure. He suggested that they might want to choose a name for their daughter, as referring to her in numerical terms made her appear more experiment than human, although the operation was, in itself, a bit of an experiment, as it hadn't been carried out on many infants previously.

'Her name's Clare,' said Bill.

'Okay,' said the doctor, looking at Stella for some sort of confirmation.

But Stella wasn't listening. She was watching the nurses going off shift, their hair tied neatly back, their navy blue capes billowing in the soft summer breeze. She envied them. They seemed so young and light-hearted. They were laughing and chatting; life didn't seem heavy on their shoulders. She couldn't remember a time when she'd been so carefree, when she hadn't had to calculate her every move, when sex was fun and not just a means to an end.

'My husband'll sign all the forms,' she mumbled. 'He understands all that stuff.'

Bill shot a disapproving look her way. 'My wife's not herself today,' he said, in an attempt to remove the expression of concern from the doctor's face. 'She's tired, and anxious about the baby. I'm sure you—'

'Yes, of course,' said the doctor, accepting Bill's outward calm as ratification of his words. 'But unfortunately, Mr Hinchliffe, your daughter is seriously ill. And without surgical intervention her chances of survival are extremely low. Going on from this, as previously mentioned, no surgery is without risk, but the unstable and irregular respiration of an infant can be an added complication, as anaesthesia decompresses the cardiovascular and respiratory systems. We only advocate very light anaesthesia for very young babies, and sometimes, none at all.'

Bill rose to his feet 'No! No! No! She'll be in pain? Is that it?'

'Certainly not!' barked the doctor, his eyebrows raised. 'Please, take a seat.' And, extending the palm of his right hand, invited Bill to sit, which he did immediately, allowing the doctor to continue.

'Current medical opinion is that babies do not have sufficiently developed neural connections to feel pain in the same way as adult humans. They have very immature nervous systems, and so, in the case of your daughter, we propose the use of paralysing drugs and physical restraint.'

Bill turned to his wife, and she to him. 'I don't care what she's called,' she said.

'Okay,' continued the doctor, not catching a word of it. 'We're going to do the operation tomorrow. She's well hydrated and her breathing is regular and strong. Right,' he said, retracting the nib of his pen, 'would you like to see her first thing? Before we take her down?'

'Yes,' said Bill.

'No,' whispered Stella.

***

Stella had an 'always the flame, never the moth' approach to men: a way of weaving them into her life. But marriage and the birth of her first child had taught her that men were not to be relied upon, that emotional attachment hinders the decision-making process, clouds the issue, makes you weak, and that her happiness would now depend on a complete dislocation from her husband, her friends, and of course, her children.

There had been many an admirer coming in and out of the grocery shop she now ran with her more often than not errant, husband, but none of that really interested her until she met Drew. From Glasgow, Drew was a semi-professional boxer, a fighter by trade – the Blackhill Bruiser – who could look after himself and his woman if need be. That in itself had been quite a turn-on for Stella, who often compared him to her husband and his pathetic love for theatre, books and all things opera. His mid-brown hair framed a pale, freckly face, a kind face, not a dangerous face – not the type of face that kept a girl awake at night sick with worry, because Drew wasn't a worry. He was, however, a very easy mark. She'd known from set-off he'd a thing for her. Men usually did, and he was just how she liked her victims: uncomplicated, ignorant and completely in her thrall.

She'd lead him down the garden path, slam the door in his face and move on. She'd been doing it all her life and getting away with it, and saw no reason to change now.

'I'll tell you this,' snarled Drew, slamming down an empty glass, 'he'd better hope I don't run into him any time soon.'

Stella sighed. 'I've got to get out,' she whined. 'But he won't let me go. Says he'll kill me before he sees me with anyone else.' Which wasn't exactly true. It'd been Stella who'd screamed those words at her husband as she pinned his hand to the kitchen table with her dressmaking scissors. It was Bill who'd been rushed to hospital that night, not his wife.

'Well, like I said,' – pulling her to him with a devoted kiss – 'he hasn't met me yet, has he?' As that night, they sat in the pub making their plans. And three Babychams, four Double Diamonds and a gin and orange later, all was done.

After having her husband beaten to a pulp by a gang of thugs, Stella finally left Bill for her tattooed lover in 1965, taking one large suitcase packed with clothes, several pairs of high-heeled shoes, a Timex watch and her eyelash curlers, but unfortunately, not her children.

Yes, she'd given them life, had them growing deep inside her, had even gone through the pain and trauma of their birth, just to discard them like the broken trinket box she'd left on her bedside table. And for what? Love? It definitely wasn't love. Hate? Well yes, probably. But a man? He wasn't. The boxer might well be armour-plated, but in the end, he was just another handbag.

Going for a Fight, Dress for a Party

Sitting with Evelynne on a flatbed lorry, singing a home-made mash-up of 'You are My Sunshine', 'Did You Ever See a Dream Walking?' and 'You Were Meant for Me', as we bumped and wobbled down the cobbled street towards our new house.

She leant over, kissed my head, and with a nod and smile said, 'We're flitting now, aren't we, Clare?'

Evelynne had a soft smile which lit up her delicate face. She was my dream walking: very easy to love, beauty shone from her and, at three years old, I was already addicted to the light.

We pulled up outside 101 Thorndon Road, and the driver came round to steady her as she jumped off her perch. 'Madame, we have arrived!' he said, snatching a flat cap and bowing majestically, before kissing her hand.

'Oh, please,' sighed Evelynne, pooh-poohing his presence with a backhanded wave. 'Don't "Madame" me, it's far too ageing.' Then, turning to me, whispered, 'Cheeky varmint!' before making her way to the front door. 'Okay,' she chirped. 'Let's get everything in, done an' dusted before Granddad gets home for tea.'

She put the key into the lock and gave the tatty red door, which opened directly onto the street, a firm push, and we walked in.

Situated at the top end of the street, our 'new' house wasn't new at all, but a very old and jaded back-to-back terrace, overlooking a small and sloping higgledy, and somewhat piggledy, backyard. A luxury block of outside toilets coordinated in colour to each back door, sat centrally to its apex and a solitary tin bath, to be shared between all, hung on the wall outside ours.

Small brick walls separated yard from yard as far as the eye could see, one even playing host to a huge oak tree complete with rope and tyre – the only tree for miles, ancient and singular, but never underused. There were no bathrooms, telephones, fridges or wine racks. Carpets were a rarity and duvets hadn't been heard of, much less thrown on the bed or had days named after them and, as your average dad wouldn't have been seen dead sweating over a flat-pack, bingo was the way most people home-improved – bingo and the coupons found in cigarette packets like Benson and Hedges or Embassy Regal. So, as long as my father kept chain-smoking, that new three-piece suite could be ours by Christmas.

As well as the muck, mice and measles, we also had a fair share of spinsters. Singletons born of two world wars, the sweethearts parted by death. And there were three such battle-hardened old ladies living in our backyard: Edie and Vera, two sisters in a house-share; and Biddy Foster on the other side of the entry.

Although not technically a war widow because she'd never been married, Biddy had been engaged to a dashing young man who'd gone off to fight, but never came back.

Also, and as it goes, Biddy was no sweetheart: she was a shameless opportunist and a very accomplished actress, who faked blindness and other miscellaneous diseases in order to gain sympathy from her neighbours, who she used intermittently for the free-loading of hot dinners, complementary TV and assistance with the odd bucket of coal.

Although Biddy did have dodgy lamps – one down the shops, the other coming back with the change – blind she was not.

Always immaculately dressed, and never missing a shampoo and set on pensioners' Wednesdays, with her blue rinse protected by a beaded hairnet, and armed with her twin set and pearls, she'd rattle up and down the street, waving her white stick from side to side, smacking the living shit out of anyone who got in her way. No, you could never describe Biddy as a 'people person'.

'I always keep mi hat on int house. If it's sumdy I like, I've just got in; if it's sumdy I don't, I'm just off out.'

Funnily enough, no one ever did call on Biddy, well, not voluntarily that is, mainly because she was a violent age-rager, with a face like a well-kept grave, and so many wrinkles in her forehead - rumour was: the hat was a screw-on.

Her wishbone legs were low slung and bandy; she couldn't stop a pig in an entry, but she could definitely bone one in the dark.

Evelynne took pity on her from time to time, cooking her dinners and, when the weather was really cold and dismal, invited her to our house to watch TV.

Having spent her youth in the roaring twenties, Biddy appreciated glamour and, surgical stockings aside, her passion for turban jewellery, ruby port and bottom-drawer light entertainment had never waned. Her preferred viewing was an eclectic mix of: gratuitous religion - *Stars on Sunday*; colonial racism - *The Black and White Minstrel Show*; knitwear appreciation - *Val Doonican*; and hair-style envy - *Danny La Rue*.

'Just look at them beautiful gowns,' she'd swoon. 'You can hardly believe it's a man can you, Evelynne?' Then, remembering she was supposed to be half-blind, 'Is it a man, Evelynne?'

'Oh, yes,' sighed Evelynne. It's definitely a man. He's got hands like shovels an' walks like he's got summat trapped!'

Which wasn't exactly true. Danny La Rue was a woman, I was almost sure of it. In any event, he was the man who made the man in Biddy feel more like a woman. 'Wonder who does his shampoo an' set then, Evelynne?'

'Wouldn't want to hazard a guess at that one. But I think we can safely say you won't be running into him at Vanessa's on Wednesday.'

Evelynne knew that Biddy wasn't exactly 'knitting wi both needles', that she was a first-rate user and, when she was out of earshot, would snap, 'It's a day's work just looking at her. She gets where watter can't, wi her four faces an' a swinging head!' (me neither), but also told us that Biddy belonged to something called 'The Lost Generation', and that at just eighteen years old her fiancé, a voluntary enlister, untrained and unprepared for life on the battlefield, had been brutally cut down in the summer of 1916, leaping from the trenches to die on his knees, on the very first day of that bloodiest of battles, the Battle of the Somme. She said that Biddy's heart was broken, but her pain was silent. That we should learn to look deeper, always be kind, and accept Biddy, blind warts an' all.

And that was the thing about Evelynne: she was a very straight arrow, honest, caring and genuine in her kindness. She wore her wisdom lightly and people loved her for it. She enjoyed gossip, but never dished it gratuitously. She had a convenient conduit in friend and neighbour Dame Mavis Butterall for that.

Mavis lived in the house at the opposite corner of our yard, she too was a slave to 'the Bidster'. On washdays (Mondays and Thursdays), Evelynne and Mavis would lean on our windowsill in their slippers and pinnies with a cup of builders' tea and a box of broken biscuits, gassing, usually about the neighbours or how many Green Shield stamps they had and what they were going to squander them on.

Mavis, a chubby delight, was partial to dying her grey hair pillar-box red, the type of red that never really looks authentic. Her flowered wrap overalls protectively layered garish Crimplene dresses, festooned in acid-toned psychedelic patterns, combustible and a real danger to the epileptic minority – the jumble sale had just exploded and Mavis was inside.

Her husband, Ronnie, had also been a soldier, fighting in the Second World War, and had fallen victim to a mustard-gas attack, which in later life had left him with a terminal lung disease.

Their only son and heir, Tricky Micky, a George Best doppelgänger, was always in and out of prison for petty crime. He was also a hapless alcoholic but, due to his good looks, a professional shagger of many women, who seemed to be on a constant conveyor belt in and out of his bedroom, usually after an afternoon session at the Corner Pin. The aptly titled 'Kitty City' faced onto our backyard, and was decorated in wall-to-wall hardcore porn: tits and fannies everywhere. He was a slave to the kitten, a real pussy-hunter and, like most turbo-shagging fanny addicts, totally disabled by it.

Yes, these were the people in my 'new' backyard, living their lives on just one of a hundred little streets running through the main artery and beating heart of Pitsmoor, all with a shop on both corners. Beer-offs, chippies, cobblers and pubs made up the microcosm in which we lived, with Main Street Spital Hill a mile or so up the road, offering up more no-nonsense fair-trade shopping, from elegant attire to pint pots for tea, and a vast array of working men's clubs in a community that had, quite frankly, seen it all, but funnily enough, never once sat back on its fat backside.

The Albion Hotel, a Spital Hill landmark, was the most infamous pub in Pitsmoor. It was Rasta Central and always heaving. You felt the dub long before you could hear it, and if you could hear it, you certainly weren't a local.

This was no ordinary pub: we could buy anything here, and there was nothing that couldn't be sourced. The Albion, never knowingly out-stocked, brought us most of life's essentials: fags, drugs, clothes, mood rings, electric blankets, fan heaters, rent boys, haberdashery, fruit and veg, prostitutes, mousetraps and various other household items.

Also, and for those recently suffering the trauma of a burglary, you could buy your own property back at a very reasonable rate – a sort of car boot sale, before car boot sales had even been invented, or anyone really owned a car.

There was usually a fight over one thing or another, and like the wild Wild West, someone often left by the frosted window, taproom side, with a three hundred kilohertz hardcore accompaniment.

The police arrived (usually too late). The police left. And it all started again.

Evelynne took me everywhere with her, but my favourite trips were always to the shops on Spital Hill when she'd buy me a gingerbread man for the short walk home.

I loved watching the Rastas. To me, they were like exotic pirates, swinging their dreads, drawing on blow and clicking their fingers to a beat of their own. No one stressed the Rastarfari and right here, right now, holding Evelynne's hand, I was Rasta too.

'Alright, Mrs H, how ya doin?' came a soft breezy Jamaican drawl.

'Hello, Charles, I'm fine. How are you? How's your mum?'

'I'm good, Mrs H, good. Sitting on dubs. Mi mutha still can't win at bingo tho.' He kissed his teeth and shot me a smile.

This was Charles Gayle, seventeen years old and perhaps the most beautiful boy in the whole wide world. He was tall and slim, with perfect white teeth, which spread the width of his good-looking face whenever he turned on his charming smile. His waist-length locks were

27

covered today by a hand-knitted hat, which bore the colours of Marcus Garvey and the Ethiopian flag distorting his head to the size of a pumpkin.

Charles worked the night shifts at Firth Brown and spent his rest days hanging with his friends, smoking ganja, drinking Guinness and dancing for the girls as they walked on by. 'Hey, baby, mi fixed on you, what ya sei?' His sexy dark voice made the white girls giggle, albeit with a flattered swoon.

Still chewing the gingerbread, I stood behind Evelynne, too shy to meet his eyes. I too had been whacked by the Gayle stick of charm.

'Hey, baby.' Fixed on me now.

I moved further behind Evelynne's legs.

He took the spliff out of his mouth. 'One day wi get some wax on dis, mek some proper locks, shape you up.' He put his hand on my long red hair, shaking it hard with a laugh. 'Where ya off?'

I couldn't speak, so Evelynne replied for me. 'We're off home. She likes Hammy Hamster so we've got to get back.'

'Ahh, *River Bank Tales* is it?' He looked at me again and I almost puked. 'Might need to avoid di corner dere tho, Mrs H.' He nodded towards the Albion. 'Dere's bin some sort of an incident.'

'No worse than most days.'

'Guess not.' He laughed. 'Drama, always drama.'

'Alright, Charles, see you later. Tell Pansy I'll see her Tuesday if she's going.'

'Yeah, might get di jackpot, Mrs H, might even get di jackpot! She wants tu clout dat caller. Allus his fault when she dunt win. Sez he's a fart in a cullender!' He laughed, huge and bellowing, putting his amazing smile back on display once more. I thought I was going to die, I loved him so much.

'Stop staring, Clare. Take my hand, hold it tight.' Evelynne was serious of voice and I always did what I was told when this particular tone had been adopted.

We walked on.

It was a sunny Friday lunchtime and, as usual, we were heading off home for another action-packed episode of *Tales of the Riverbank.* I held on to Evelynne with one hand and my gingerbread man with the other, mulling the logistics of what rodent training on a level such as this might entail, thinking, it can't be easy teaching a ferret to squeeze a tune from a full set of bagpipes, or directing bad-tempered gerbils on the intricacies of two-litre sports cars, and just how, in the name of sweet Johnny Morris, d'you get a hamster to handle a four-speed riverboat? Yep, it was worthy of a side eye, as I chewed a leg and swallowed hard.

As we got close to the Albion, however, things were not as usual; it was not the same.

A small crowd was huddled outside around something hidden from view, when Evelynne squeezed my hand, and ordered me to 'Walk a bit faster', as now, through gaps in the coats of the people there gathered, I could see a black woman. She looked in some pain. Her hair, which wasn't in any particular style, was crowned with a fur hat: a faux leopard-skin hat, matched to the collar and cuffs of her coat. She was sitting on a chair, but facing the wrong way. Her chest was propped against the back of the chair, her arms hugging it tight, her mouth was open, but her eyes were closed. I couldn't make it out – why on earth was she sitting like that? A few steps on however, and all came clear, well, that's when I saw it: a six-inch blade sticking right in the middle of her back, pinning the coat with the fake-fur trim to her body, like an announcement on a noticeboard.

The crowd waited as an ambulance approached, but no one so much as uttered a word. I suppose someone must have come to her aid by sitting her back to front on the chair, but still, there she sat, silently waiting to be saved.

I bit into the left arm, mumbling, 'She's still wearing her hat,' as Evelynne squeezed again and we picked up the pace.

A flat cap and a raincoat was on the approach. 'By eck,' he said, 'we might not be rich, but we do see life.'

'We certainly do,' sighed Evelynne, nodding her sweet smile. We were walking much faster now.

***

As winter approached, tin-bath bathing in front of a three-filter gas fire proved a dangerous luxury, as a result of the skin-to-bath contact fireside. So, ever mindful of third-degree burns, Evelynne would pack us off to the slipper baths instead.

The Sutherland Road slipper baths were a designated bathing area segregated from the main swimming pool. Each private cubical contained a huge bath, for the use of families who didn't have bathrooms and, like us, needed a weekly scrub.

Every Saturday, Frances and I would set off with a bar of carbolic soap and a bottle of Vosene rolled up in a threadbare towel to spend the afternoon at the slipper baths, not leaving until our fingers crinkled like frozen chips, or the fat hairy-faced attendant thumped on the door with her equally fat fists, shouting, 'Come on, you two, out! Sumdy's waiting on this!'

'I bet she's been looking at our fannies,' whispered Frances. 'She's a lesbian.' I nodded in agreement, but the truth of it was, although I knew what a fanny was, the word 'lesbian' was completely lost on me, as we took the short walk home with wet hair, which had frozen solid by the time we got in.

Saturday night was also pie night, and while I loved Evelynne's meat and potato pie, I wasn't overly keen on the side of sprouts she insisted on serving. Apart from occasionally going the wrong side of egg, there wasn't much I wouldn't eat. But sprouts? Really? They tasted like iron railings and had the look of a budgie's head about them.

'Budgie's head!' squawked Evelynne. 'Don't be so ridiculous. It's a sprout! Where's … where's the beak?'

At this stage, it's probably worth pointing out that the three compulsory activities as far as my grandmother was concerned were: work, voting and eating vegetables. Therefore, I was told in no uncertain terms that it would be in my best interests to shut my own beak and swallow them down without further comment. So, rather than cause any unwanted teatime friction, I did – I closed my eyes and necked the budgie.

And now, part of my post slipper-bath duties included a trip to the corner shop for the Henderson's Relish to lay as garnish to the budgies' heads and pie – a simple task on paper, but one fraught with risk and danger in reality.

It's not that I courted danger or got into many fights. In fact, I hadn't been in trouble for months, not since I'd painted Kitty Clarke's face tomato-red during a violently charged 'art for the under sevens', after she'd accused my father of murdering my mother. And to be honest, even Evelynne agreed she'd had that one coming.

No, you didn't have to go looking for trouble; you just encountered it by straying onto the wrong patch, or associating with the 'wrong gang'.

Again, the law according to Evelynne dictated that it was easy to run with the crowd, but much braver to stand up for something you believed in, even if you were standing alone: a philosophy that always left me herding with those considered to be outside the norm.

My best friend and partner in crime lived just across the street and, like me, Dolan (Dolly) O'Brian was a bit of a funeral groupie at the numerous 'in-house' wakes that took place on our street from time to time. In fact, that's how we met, at a coffin file-past.

I'd been very attracted by his hard-to-please attitude and the Moon Wind perfume he'd taken to wearing for end-of-life events. We'd stand at the back, me in a plastic nurse's hat I got free in *Twinkle*, him in a 'Slade in Flame' T-shirt, feigning sorrow and regret with the rest of the mourners, listening intently to pre-death tales of the much-loved deceased – all very educational and emotionally nourishing stuff.

'Big dog's cock! Little cat's fanny! The sherry's complete shite!' He spat, hand on hip, but necking it all the same. 'Come on,' he ordered, slamming down the glass, which appeared to contain a fine Scotch whisky. 'I'm sure I saw some Angel Delight: banana, methinks.'

We made our way into the kitchen, but the curtains were still drawn until after the funeral, so it was hard seeing the hand in front of your face, never mind dessert.

'I like you,' he said, with a narrow stare. 'You're not bad for someone with no top lip. In fact, why don't we just run away to Ireland, an' become professional wailers? Seriously, we'd be checkin some right chump!'

'I'm not sure. I'm not that good at crying to order.' I couldn't see

Angel Delight; his snorkel must have malfunctioned.

'Maybe not,' he said, now scanning my body, 'although dressed like that, you could always audition for *The Little Match Girl*.' He lifted a lock of my long red hair. 'Urggghhhhh.'

He shuddered, never unintentionally rude or missing an opportunity to lacerate – a quality I quite admired, even then.

***

Now, I went to Sunday school just like everyone else, but our church, the Gower Street Wesleyan Reform, was very traditional, very Church of England, and very dull.

Conversely, Dolan's family were devout and Catholic (although the hymns he preferred to sing were those penned by Saint Dolly of Parton, hence his nickname). Still, Catholic was where it was at. I so wanted to be Catholic, all smells and bells and glamorous to the point of exotic. His sister Peggy had worn a wedding dress and taken confirmation (whatever that was), they both went to midnight mass, Priests came to their house wearing rosary beads, swinging them side to side, chanting 'Hail Mary' and 'Our Father'. It just didn't seem fair at all.

His mother, Mary, was a sexy Irish woman with short dark hair, a slim frame and a fantastic pair of legs. She wore high-heeled shoes at all times, even when hoovering the house, and although she'd given birth to several children, her body bore no trace, shrinking right back into shape as if by magic. She was married to Patrick, a dark curly-haired hunk of a man, who had a thick Irish accent and a thick Irish moustache to match.

It'd been blatantly clear from the outset that Dolly had been whacked by the lavender bush. A first-class hogger of the limelight who liked to hang around the girls, he was addicted to fierce, unpredictable melodrama and, in addition to funerals, had a particular fondness for musical theatre, exotic footwear, and dressing up, with the ever-resourceful Hyacinth, a shiny little girl from a few doors down, providing the wardrobe.

In a dazzling array of her mothers' old dresses, we'd dance around the backyard, while Dolly sang a medley of Rodgers and Hammerstein classics.

Of course, when it came to a more demanding role, he insisted on being the leading lady every time. His list of characters included Joan Crawford (Mildred Pierce), Vivienne Leigh (Blanch DuBois) and Bette Davis (Margo Channing). We'd act out parts from *What Ever Happened to Baby Jane* – in which he gave some of his most convincing performances, even crushing the finger of my left hand in the Joan Crawford kicking scene (then again, he had been in character for that one all his life) – and *Sunset Boulevard* when, just like Norma Desmond, 'We didn't need dialogue, we had faces.'

Also, and not wanting to be outdone by his sister's Holy Communion outfit, Dolly had a penchant for the wedding dress Hyacinth's mother had given us to play in. He paired it with his mother's pink satin stilettos and used to run up and down the street singing Shirley Bassey songs. So, trust me when I say, there really was no top he couldn't go over.

'I'm singing Maria today,' spat Dolly, tugging the wedding dress from Hyacinth's tightly clenched fists.

'I don't think so, Mrs Bumlaugh. It's my turn, my dress and my part!' Hyacinth wasn't scared of his razor tongue or his diamond-encrusted temper.

'Give me the fucking dress, Desna.' (He always called her Desna when he wanted a reaction. Desna was a girl at our school, who'd been expelled for breaking a dinner lady's arm during a Clackers confiscation incident. She was a real hind beast, the polar opposite of Hyacinth.) 'Or wavey goodbye to the fucking blue sandals.' Hands on hips, he meant it, but Hyacinth wasn't moving until … 'I mean it, Desna. Ya won't be squeezing dem trotters in um dis side o' Christmas!'

With that, Hyacinth let go of the dress. 'Alright, you big cream cake, have it!' She knew he wasn't bluffing with the blue sandal threat. They were his mother's best shoes and on occasion he'd sneak them out of her closet for Hyacinth to wear in her role of Maria.

'Get it right, sista! Puff! Cream bloody puff! You tick or sumtin?' His Jamaican accent was dreadful but, with the wedding dress slung casually over his shoulder, he continued: 'Leen di baggi an' get dere wi di pump in!' which sent Hyacinth into hysterics. Her brother

Charles (he of the good face) had taught Dolly tiny snips of patois and told him that the 'Leen di baggi' thing meant 'Stick it up yer fat arse!' Untrue, of course – even I knew that, when strictly translated, it actually meant: 'Bend over while I shag you from behind.' Nevertheless, I wasn't about to put him right. He'd find out for himself and soon enough, no doubt about that.

Hyacinth kissed her teeth, took an alternative costume from the dressing-up bag, and we continued with our truncated version of *West Side Story*, unaware we had an audience.

Barry Bankes had been watching from the other end of the street, and he wasn't exactly a fan. The Bankeses were a formidable family. Barry's mother, Regina, was, to coin a phrase, 'As hard as a fag-smoker's artery'.

Dolly said that, 'If she were in Russia she'd be pulling a plough.' She had a face like a blind cobbler's thumb and a gaspy raspy accent, born from years of smoking Parky Roughs.

Her hair, a dyed-black beehive up-do, made her look like a female Elvis (not in his heyday – more towards the nappy period of his life). She wore Crimplene miniskirts, which skimmed her chunky thighs, and forty-denier ecru tights that did nothing to hide the fireside tartan that had scorched her legs, teamed with white, all-weather, but not leather, peep-toed plastic sandals. Her arse was like a collapsed mineshaft and her tight acrylic crew-neck jumpers outlined the rolls of fat, from her large breasts to the two stomachs she appeared to have. Her look was completed by a pale-pink frosted lipstick, which framed her tobacco-stained teeth.

Gina didn't work and her husband (the aptly named Robbie) was always in and out of prison, only returning between crimes to give her the odd black eye. He was 'away' when his youngest daughter, Sharon, was run over and killed, leaving Gina to raise her remaining six children alone.

Gina had a hard life, which in turn had made her hard. She fought with the neighbours and was rarely seen reversing out of a fight without the red furry high-heeled slippers she often used to beat the living shit out of anyone who criticised her feral brood.

Barry, her third-born, had no front teeth, which created a dull buzz whenever he spoke. This speech impediment meant he was always getting in and out of fights when anyone mentioned the 'B' word, and sometimes just chinning you on the pre-emption.

As I said, Dolly, Hyacinth and I were in our usual spot on the spare ground next to the old garages, and were halfway through 'There's a Place for Us' when we heard the familiar rant of 'Thucking puths, an' thake twaths'. I turned to see Barry and four angry underweight boys heading towards us, their walk getting faster and faster until they broke into a sprint. Barry was at the front of the mob with a stick, which he threw on his approach.

Dolly, never missing an opportunity to perform, pulled the wedding dress up over his thighs and, in another fabricated life moment, started to scream, 'Oh no! We're all going to die! Someone help! Help us! Please!'

I, on the other hand, was quite prepared to stay and fight. Having scanned the options for possible escape routes and found them wanting, I'd decided early doors that the only way round this shit, was straight through it. Besides, I wasn't taking orders from Buzzin Baz and his ridiculous gang of prepubescent pugilists any time soon; I was half Yardie and no one, I mean no one, was calling on my fake blood.

But Dolly, having the spine of a banana, decided to turn, take flight and run. I'd expected nothing less: he'd never been a team player, and apart from that, his hair was the only girl he'd ever really loved. His spindly legs looked just like old ladies' as he sprinted down the street in pink stilettos, holding the wedding dress over his waist, screaming something Catholic, and in Latin for extra effect.

Unfortunately, one satin heel became lodged in a grate, sending him hurtling to the ground, smack bang on his leather. He looked so small and insignificant sprawled out on the tarmac, legs akimbo, the wedding dress over his head, like a discarded fairy from the tattered remains of a threadbare tree the tinsel had long since forgot.

The last thing I saw before I felt the first blow, was a pink heel in a black grate and I knew the broken shoe was going to hurt my treacherous friend much more than the beating he was about to take.

Co-dependency Begins at Home

It's hard being the unwanted item in any bagging area, but for me, that's how life began, the scar on my stomach a constant reminder of the life-curdling disappointment of some human beings and their grimy need for self-preservation.

So, despite a sometimes questionable loyalty, there was still a lot to recommend Dolly.

His infinite capacity for the fantasy of self-delusion had been born from a raging insecurity. He wore vicious retorts like an armour, protecting a soft-hearted more vulnerable self. He was odd and therefore always out; he could give, but couldn't take, stampeding stage left at the slightest whiff of a confrontation.

Dolly needed a minder, and to this end, I was happy to have received a couple of black eyes defending his honour, in what can only be described as marathon bouts of proper, stand-up, bare-fist fighting. I didn't share his capricious fair-weathered approach to friendship and, being a master tactician of the brawl, was neither stifled nor scared when it came to simple bacteria like boys. No, there was only one person that could strike the fear of fuckery and dereliction into me, and that person was my father.

He could cut you down with words which hit hard, scarred deep and had a longevity no punch in the face could match. He was unpredictable and that terrified me, particularly when he'd been drinking and became totally out of control.

An unspoken rule in our house was: you will *never*, and we mean *ever*, not even in a moment of extreme and utter madness, *never ever* will you discuss … the Birth Mother.

We were not allowed to ask where she was, what she looked like, whether she was dead or alive. We had no photographs upon which to rely. She was an empty space as far as we were concerned. So, like most abandoned children, we'd painted-in our own versions from our vivid imaginations, until one day, the mother I hadn't even met decided she would poke my father with a shitty-stick and send me and my sisters

36

Christmas presents.

It was January and the 'gifts' had arrived late. This had been a tactical move on her part, I think: with the frenzied atmosphere of Christmas Day masking the impact, a January delivery was best.

It must have been a Saturday, because my father was not at work. He'd taken a job as a long-distance lorry driver after she'd left, in order to pay off his debts and support us, something he resented and wore like a badge whenever in the midst of an alcoholic mood swing.

I was opening my presents with Frances and we were excited on three levels. Firstly, as little girls we were giddy about the expensive dolls and books she'd sent. Secondly, I'd never had the pleasure, having been just eighteen months old when she'd disappeared, so this 'having a mum' thing was a bit of a bonus, particularly if she was going to start turning up with dolls and things like that. Plus, it had crossed my mind that Kitty Clarke might have been onto something with the old murder theory. Not now though, in the face of such overwhelming evidence that she, 'the Mother', was alive, yes alive, and possibly shopping at Redgates.

Needless to say, the light relief in finding out my father wasn't a murderer was short-lived to a certain extent.

I'd just ripped the last of the wrapping from the last of the presents when he entered the room, and having read the 'Love from Mummy' tag in the misguided hope that she actually cared – effervescing with fun and excitement, duly lit the touchpaper and screeched, 'Dad! Dad! Look what my mummy's sent!'

Silence fell and I knew instantly what I'd done. But it was too late. I couldn't rewind, scramble the words back into my stupid little gob, swallow them hard, while slinging the gifts over my shoulder, into the dog's basket and out of sight. No, fuck me, I'd just dropped the 'M-bomb', and now I was about to pay.

I couldn't decide whether to run or pretend to faint but, before the minute cogs in my piddling little pea-brain had time to turn, he'd already started towards me, placing huge hands onto my bony little shoulders, his grip getting tighter and tighter as he started to shake my tiny, underweight (some might say *emaciated*), six-year-old body. His glare intensified as, through gritted teeth, fag breath and bile he began, 'Well, you'd better get rid of them, or your *daddy* won't love you any more. Do you understand?'

I could feel the familiar burn of tears starting to well as I tried hard to recover with, 'But, I was only—'

He came back. 'I've just told you, *stupid*. Get rid of them or your daddy won't love you any more.'

My sister Frances stood as still and turgid as a statue, her gaze frozen, not daring to move, as my father slumped to his knees, put his head in his hands and started to weep.

Elizabeth, my eldest sister (a sly opportunist), fell onto him screaming, 'I hate her! I hate her, daddy! I don't want her presents.' She had a way of saying the right things at the right time: brown-nosing was her strong point and main focus in life. By creating this fiction of love, she knew exactly how to work my father, and both being fully paid-up members of the GIT union, were so alike.

Evelynne started to undo her pinny. 'Come on, girls. Put your coats on an' we'll go for a walk.'

Elizabeth was so far up his arse we could only just see the soles of her pink furry slippers, so I presumed she wasn't coming with us. 'I can't, Nan,' she cried in the very latest crocodile style. 'I can't leave my dad here on his own.' She really was a piece of work, and if I hadn't been so terrified I'd have given her a standing ovation with a rose between my teeth, as my father put his loving arms around her, pulling her to him like a ragdoll, kissing her hard and squeezing her tight.

But Evelynne was determined to defuse. 'Well, get your balaclavas on then, you two, an' let's have a walk.'

I looked at Frances and she at me. We took our coats from the bottom of the stairs and, pulling our balaclavas over our heads, walked out with Evelynne into the cold afternoon, like a bonsai version of the SAS.

On the brainstorming walk of shame, we decided we'd pack the presents up into carrier bags and give them to some other children on the street. If we got them out of the house maybe, just maybe, he'd calm his daft self down. Not only was he overreacting, he was really spoiling our fun. I hadn't seen a doll of that quality for some time – it was borderline Tippy Tumbles. I'd mulled with the idea of hiding it in the outside toilet, but couldn't take the chance of it being discovered, and so grudgingly had agreed to let it go.

In retrospect, however, this was never going to be a big enough gesture for the narcissist. No, he was going to drain as much drama and attention out of this as he could.

Since his divorce, my father had become hateful of his children, making us feel like it was our fault she'd left, our fault she'd come back. No, he was going to suck the very marrow out of us and beat us into emotional submission come what may, as upon our return, with a huge knot in a very small stomach, I decided to move in for a cuddle, but he grabbed my tiny wrists hard and tight, pushing me back with a stab. 'I've just told you,' he snarled, 'your daddy doesn't love you any more.' Then, dissolving my innards with a 'Why did I have such thick kids?' the indignant dad bastard left the room.

***

The silent treatment continued for some time, along with some parental knife-twisting: being extra-fatherly to Elizabeth, while at the same time ignoring the existence of me and Frances. He didn't speak nor would he be spoken to: we were invisible as far as my father was concerned. After a while, however, we became immune to his mental torture, as we reached what can only be described as some sort of stress plateau. So, short of sleep deprivation or being waterboarded there wasn't really much else he could do to hurt us – he decided to turn up the stress meter by taking the first option.

One night, I awoke to the sound of thunderous steps running up the stairs. My little heart began to bang so hard, my body had started to lift with each and every pulse. The message from my terror antenna was that something nasty was about to happen. It was then that the door burst open wide and the smell of fags and alcohol wafted into the room, shortly followed by my father, fresh from the pub, off his tits and out of control, which for a psychotic lunatic is never a good look.

Frances, who was asleep next to me, suddenly jolted awake and in unison we dived under the sheets for cover, as he went lunging over to the window. Elizabeth, whose bed was situated beneath it, had also taken cover under the sheets.

I wanted to get up and run but my body was so paralysed by fear I just couldn't move, so I slipped the sheets down under my chin, to get an estimation of his exact position, in order that I could plan the escape route for me and Frances – Elizabeth was on her own.

Looking out into the dark room, I could see the outline of his tall frame against the glow of the streetlight as he pulled the curtains apart and began screaming into the night.

'Why me? Why me? What have I done to deserve this?'

He turned and pointed towards our bed. Frances was still under the covers clinging to my bony little body, but I, like a fool, was staring right at him unable to move. I knew instinctively that I shouldn't make eye contact. Tactically, it's aggressive and quite the wrong thing to do, unless of course you're a heavyweight boxer about to start round one. No, in this situation the eye of the tiger was only going to inflame things.

Suddenly, his black eyes caught mine and, with that, he launched himself onto our bed. 'I'll tell you this,' he grunted, grabbing Frances from under the covers, her hands clamped over her head, body in the foetal position. 'I'll tell you this for nothing!' He threw her back and grabbed me by the throat of my Bri-Nylon nightie, shaking me so hard that my oversized eyes in my undersized head began to rattle in their sockets. 'You won't be calling anyone else *Dad*! I'll kill you before that happens! D'you hear me?' My head now slamming against the padded plastic headboard, the collar of my nightie getting tighter and tighter around my scrawny little neck.

His face was so close, I could see the keloid-like veins bulging on his forehead. He smelt of too many fags, too much gin. His spittle was spraying my face with the pronouncement of each and every exaggerated word: a handsome man, so ugly now.

Just as I was about to slip into unconsciousness due to a complete lack of oxygen, he let me go with a push and stood up, taking off his sheepskin coat and throwing it onto the floor like a spoilt five-year-old. Then, after wiping the tears with the back of his hands, he began pulling at the front of his shirt, sending the buttons flying across the room, mumbling over and over again, 'I'll kill you. Then I'll kill me.' He was pointing to his chest, just in case we weren't sure who the 'me' was.

Moments later, he fell back onto our bed crying and squeezing us too hard, as my cod eyes caught his and he started again, more coherent this time: 'It's not easy this, doll face.' (He never called me Clare.) 'When you have kids you'll understand, it's not easy.'

I couldn't move, I was still finding it hard to breathe, and after the staring thing had set him off, thought it best to keep my trap shut.

'Who'd have kids,' he cried. 'Who'd have 'em? When all they do is break your heart!'

Quite frankly, right now, I was thinking who'd have fucking parents? They stifle your toy collection, question your cerebral heft, turn up pissed and emotionally out of control in the middle of the night, rattling your eye sockets and threatening to kill you. So, if anyone, and I mean anyone, was at the hinterland of their frigging devotion, that person was most definitely me!

But … he was the father: he had the power and his power had a currency all of its own.

I was the child: a child with nothing to bargain with. Defusing the madness was the only option open to me now, as I put my arms around his neck and whispered gently to his ear. 'Don't cry, Daddy.'

There was a silence, as he turned to meet me once more, the orange glow from the streetlight illuminating a face swollen by the angry tears that had poured from his bloodshot eyes. He forced a quiet laugh. 'Thick kids,' he said, roughing up my hair. 'Thick flippin' kids … an intelligent man like me.' Before falling into his sleep as the tears quickly dried.

These psychotic episodes continued to blight for quite some time. Standing outside our bedroom door for hours on end, smoking his cigarettes, listening to see if we mentioned 'the Birth Mother'. We never did; we knew he was there.

I wasn't taking any chances with the 'I'll kill you' shit either. I honestly thought he would kill us one day; it was just a matter of time. I always thought he'd take me first, so as a precaution I'd wrap Frances's nightdress around my hands, fastening to her safety net, securing to her anchor, bound as we were in this co-dependent fear.

Evelynne spent most of the night talking him down, until eventually he returned to his own bed in the early hours of the morning and I crept into hers, safe to fight another day.

***

Unfortunately, the dilemmata with the delinquent pater was just about to get worse. When in another diversion on the road to self-worth, the Birth Mother, now more settled with her second husband, decided to up the ante and take my father to court on the grounds of cruelty and neglect, claiming he was violent, controlling, hateful and abusive.

The judge, however, took the opposite view, sensibly observing that she might be in a bit of a glasshouse of her own, given that she was the 'mother' who'd abandoned her children, before giving them away to the violent, controlling, abusive *him*. And although she wasn't awarded custody, she did get visiting rights, on a biweekly basis.

For the six-year-old me, seeing her for the very first time was a strange, opaque, slow-motion affair. She was beautiful, slim and exquisitely dressed, holding her long black hair away from her face as she bent to kiss my lips. Her pale-pink frosted lipstick smelt sweet and she tasted like perfume and violets. Yes, she was definitely alive and wearing industrial supplies of Avon at each and every visit – usually in Woolworths' café – when she was always accompanied by her husband, a very unattractive Scottish bloke with curly brown hair, a busted nose and copious ears protruding from his head, like the ugly, overused handles of a heavy-set fill pot. Also in attendance was a replacement three-for-one: her new child; a little boy called Stephan.

In truth, we didn't really want to see her. Let's face it, nobody likes a tourist and my father went wobble-fish banana every time we met. It had been the catalyst for all the bouts of his drunken abuse. The emotional trauma and build-up to her visits were unbearable, my eyeballs were on my cheeks and while ever she was in our lives it was only going to continue.

Thankfully, a few months later, her mission accomplished and totally bored with the Bill-baiting routine, the Birth Mother's biweekly contact ceased and she disappeared back into the ether, never to return.

Bodyeveryself

There's nothing wrong with different, it is merely a label, and a subjective one at that, although some interpret 'different' as an indication that somewhere along the line a design fault occurred to render something – or someone – different, particularly when afraid or threatened by something or someone they don't particularly understand.

As for *being* 'different', no one ever thinks they're plugged into the wrong socket until someone else makes them feel that way.

A label is very hard to shake off and can lead to many misunderstandings that, in turn, may affect an individual's ability to function in certain areas of life.

On the other hand, some labels can be extremely helpful: they set the boundaries of 'I am me' and 'you are you'; they allow us to identify another person with a certain job, a distinguishing feature, or indeed some incident that rendered them particularly brave or stupid within the locality.

An example of this type of label can be found in all walks of life, and on the street where I lived, there were many: Vanessa the hairdresser; Pensioners' Wednesdays; Eddie the Gate, worked the weighbridge at Firth Brown; and Pub Watch Pete, who was issued with a lifetime ban from the Corner Pin after a toe-sucking incident involving the wife of his best friend (someone definitely left by the tap-room-window that night).

Then there was Mick the Rapist, a local taxi driver who took other methods of payment from female passengers falling short of the fare, as opposed to Tricky Micky, who had issues surrounding honesty and theft. Chuck-a-Chair Charlie did exactly what he said on the tin, and Lip Trot would never stop talking. Steaming Jean was the fastest ironer this side of Rotherham, and Front Lumps Freddie was a man with tits, as opposed to Fred the Feck, whose face blended with his neck. There was Steve the Snunkey, a slimy, vulgar little man, half-snake half-monkey, in contrast with Chinese Steve, who never opened his eyes. Cow's Head completely defied gravity, and Glad Eyes cried (a lot). Shire Horse Shazza had very hairy ankles, and finally, no one wanted to get stuck at a party with Bomb Scare – a bloke so dull, he could clear a room just by entering.

No, not one of these descriptors was meant to cause offence; they simply made for easier identification in the corner shop, washhouse or other public place.

Then there was Peter Ronald Carter.

Peter was my friend. I loved him. In fact, Peter was loved by everyone, from the kids on the street to the old ladies at the bingo. Even Mrs Turner who ran the penny tray at the corner shop loved him, and she could fall out with herself in a phone box.

Peter was forty-five years old, had never been married and was born in the little house on Thorndon Road where he still lived with his mother whom, now very elderly, he cared for.

His mother had suffered very much during childbirth; the midwife had to use forceps, leaving Peter with a left-sided palsy, some slurred speech and a slight, but slow, laborious gait. As a result of her experience, Peter's mother had decided on no more children, and after his father had been killed in an accident at work, Peter and his mother became inseparable. He was her world, and she, his.

I loved spending time with Peter. We'd sit on the corsey edge for hours on end chatting bubbles, writing our names in the melted summer tar with sharpened lollipop sticks, his shiny bald pate roasting in the hot summer sun. His shirts were always buttoned to the neck: short sleeves in summer; long sleeves and a knitted tank in winter. He wore belted trousers at all times (usually beige) and white socks with shiny leather shoes.

He'd shout, 'Shuttheegobori'llshutitforthee' and 'Isitourbabbyharry?' Poking fun with connective nouns at his own broad Yorkshire accent, which made him laugh hysterically. 'Thas got tu flatten thee vowels to gerrit just reight,' he'd explain with a wink, 'as opposed tu flattening thee bowels, which is summut else entirely!'

Although Peter worked part-time at the wool shop, his main occupation was running errands for the neighbours, and as such he was never without his grey nylon shopper, in which he kept his songbook – the latest copy of *Disco 45*. He knew all the words to the top twenty hits, and loved *Top of the Pops* almost as much as his private shopping, which not only funded his visits to the phone box to 'Dial-a-Disc', but also allowed him to carry out some very high-level 'environmental scanning', which meant he knew everything about most people living in our street.

For instance, he knew that Mr and Mrs O'Brian were in a wife-swap situation with their best friends Tilda and Joe; that Mr Frost had a weird way with children, and would, as he put it, 'Mess with your water' if you went to his house. He knew that Rob-yee-the-Bankes was serving time in Doncatraz, and not working the oil rigs as his buck-toothed wife had intimated. He also knew that I was suffering from a rare form of emotional poverty, which had left me vulnerable and oversensitive to noise and violence.

He'd grab my nose between his finger and thumb, shaking it from side to side. 'That's never bin a nose' he'd say with a smile, 'it's a little piece on putty'. No, Peter didn't know he was plugged into the wrong socket, because he was never made to feel that way by the people who knew him, and most certainly loved him.

In much the same way, the people living in our street had no idea they were 'different', and what's more, the subject of huge debate at the local council offices, until the summer of 1974, when In-the-Know Jo announced we were about to receive notice that due to serious concerns surrounding health and social depravity, the 'slum' in which we dwelt was to be demolished, razed to the ground, and everyone living in it rehoused within the next twelve to eighteen months.

The news had spread like pneumonia, and hit most of us (excuse the pun) like a swinging brick. What did they mean 'health and social depravity'? We might have enjoyed the odd dripping-cake, drank Marvel and only ate salads on holiday, but deprived? We were not! It is an absolute truth, that not one of us to a man knew we were 'slum-dwellers' until some brass-necked nematode down at the council decided in their right-on wisdom to inform us of the fact ... and in writing! Now, how d'you like that?

I, like many others, was completely shaken by the change to come. My friends, my school, my playground and sweet shop, my precious little house and my raggedy backyard were all about to be ripped away, along with every last molecule of security I thought I might have had. And as the days turned into weeks, slowly but surely they began to shut us down. Empty houses were boarded up, daubed in black paint with the letters 'EL OFF' (electricity off) and left for the bulldozers. No longer a matter of idle council threats or words on paper, this shit was really happening, and this shit really did hurt.

So you see, I'd been so consumed by my own sense of loss, that I hadn't really given much thought to how this was going to affect Peter, although I had noticed that he wasn't exactly himself that winter.

November was cold and snow was thick on the ground. Evelynne made sure we were well insulated against the elements, feeding us porridge and dressing us in wellington boots and mandatory balaclavas for the dark early-morning walks to school.

Dolly had moved up to St John Fisher's, a Catholic parochial on the other side of town, and was spending most of his spare time in his Saturday job at the tripe factory, or in his new hobby as voyeur to the gay men cottaging in the public toilets at the Wicker Arches, so our film re-enactments had become less frequent during those cold winter weeks.

I hadn't really seen Peter, and hadn't been too concerned until Evelynne told me he'd been picked up by the police for walking the streets late at night wearing nothing but a pair of red underpants and his best black leather shoes. Given the obvious, Evelynne was worried that he might have caught a cold: 'He could have caught his death,' she wailed, 'and his shoes will be ruined, absolutely ruined! No amount of polish will get the salt out!'

See, no one was concerned about his mental health. Any previous eccentric behaviour had been offset against this latest exhibition, and so on it went. Even when he was sitting in the washhouse next to the tumble dryers, wearing three ladies' bras over his Chairman Mao jacket, shouting 'Call me Debra!', no one so much as batted an eye. He ordered a beer at the Corner Pin, dropped a pair of false teeth into the glass and mumbled, 'Watch mi pint', but for some mad reason, never came back to drink it. He wrote 'SHIT' in capital letters on Maxine Bagshaw's forehead with a big black permanent marker. She was a precocious brat and so most people thought he had a point. He had no delusions of blandure; he was

47

different that's all. And rather than destroy that difference, we had all celebrated it.

***

Christmas Eve, 1974, and as usual my sisters and I were in bed, the empty pillowcases at our feet still not yet filled, the bedroom curtains opened wide to the orange glow of the streetlight, casting its shadows on our bedroom wall.

Through my half-sleep, I recognised Peter's voice: 'Ny then! Ny then! Nose! Nose!' (He always called me 'Nose' because I had a very small nose.) 'Nose! Nose!' Louder and louder ... I got out of bed, bare feet on lino, and climbed onto the bottom of Elizabeth's bed, which was situated under the window. David Bowie, Alice Cooper and the New York Dolls gazed out from the posters that covered the walls surrounding her. She didn't wake, and was still wearing her monkey boots, having been off her tits on cider with a gang of skinheads earlier that evening.

The ice that had accumulated on the inside of the window was opaque and solid, hindering any proper view, and so, after a gargantuan effort, I managed to pull it open instead. Then, leaning onto the cold wet sill, I called out in a determined whisper. 'What? What is it?' I couldn't see him at first, so again, 'Peter! What's going on?'

He came wobbling out from the wall, took a step back into the road to see me, then stumbled forward, finally falling onto the lamp post, before kissing it quick and hugging it hard.

'Get that dog outa my garden!' he was shouting at the top of his voice. 'Get that bleedin dog outa my bleedin garden!' (He didn't have a garden; nobody did.)

'Peter!' I was still shout-whispering, trying not to wake the rest of the house. 'Peter, What's the matter? Are you alright?' I couldn't work out how he'd managed to walk the steep hill of Lyons Street without collapse. He was wasted.

'Hey up, Nose; nosy nosy nostrils.' He pointed up at me, grey shopper in hand. 'Thad better not get the sen in trouble. Thee fatthur ill thump thee wi a whip.' Now he was shout-whispering too.

'Stay there!' I ordered, half-annoyed. 'I'm coming down.'

I closed the window and, donning the pale-blue quilted dressing gown Evelynne had bought me the previous year, sneaked out of the bedroom, through the back door, down the entry and onto the street.

By the time I got to him, he was finally silent, sitting in the street and staring at the tarmac through his tired little legs. 'I'm proper bonkeynuts, aren't I?' He looked up at me, desperate tears rolling down his lovely chubby face. I sat down on the freezing pavement next to him and put my arms around his neck, kissing his big bald head. I'd never seen him cry before.

'You're not bonkers,' I soothed, linking up his arm, 'but you are acting a bit bonkeynuts tonight.'

He grabbed the end of my nose between his forefinger and thumb, shaking it from side to side. He let go and it started to run, down to my lip. Then, opening up the shopper, he pulled out a cabbage. 'He gen mi this,' he said. 'What's his name called? Big 'n' daft, he gen me this int Corner Pin. Grew it ont allotment ... He's a soft chuff.' Then, dropping it back into the bag, paused and whispered. 'Mum's got tu gu in tu a home, an' I've got tu have tests tu see if I can live wi me sen.' His eyes caught mine for a second, then fixed back onto the ground once more. 'But I don't want tu live wi'owt her. She's ... she's mi body every self.'

I didn't quite know what to say. He was distressed in a way I hadn't seen before: broken-hearted and bereft of all hope. What did he mean *tests*? Tests for what? He'd been the carer-in-chief for most of his adult life: there was nothing he couldn't or wouldn't do for his mother. Her welfare was always his concern and to take her away now would be downright unthinkable – no, there were no words. So there we sat, for what seemed like a fortnight, one not daring to look at the other, until, smiling through the tears and still attempting humour, he blurted, 'She had a coffee pot, tha knows, Nose.'

'Who?' I quizzed, deciding to go along with it.

'Mrs O. She had a coffee pot.'

'Yes, yes she did, I remember.'

'It were a real un, tha knows, Nose; a real coffee pot.'

Right. The coffee pot. Now it made sense.

Proudly displayed on the kitchen table but, funnily enough, never used, Mrs O'Brian had brought it with her from her mother's house in Ireland. It was hand-painted with a picture of a tiny canoe floating unmanned and alone on a cool, calm water. Above it, a blue sky, with streams of breaking sunlight sifting softly to its bow. Yes, I knew the wisdom of the coffee pot, so we quoted it together, and together out loud: 'Make new friends, trust but few, and always paddle in your own canoe.'

'She's gonna gu now wit rest on 'em: no more errands tut shop fot relish or green un, an tha's off an' all, wi thee little nose, off tut new house.' He turned and looked at me. Then, rising to his feet, stood for a moment, looking down the street one way and then the other, as if trying to get his bearings. I could see the silvery reflection of his tear-stained face. He was so big, so gentle, and my little heart was breaking as he slowly walked away, past all the rubble of home sweet homes already demolished in the termination project, towards his own.

Standing still for just a moment or two, he turned back round and, with a smile bellowing snot and tears, cried, 'That's not a nose, tha knows! It's a little piece on putty!'

I stood under the street lamp and watched as he faded to the night. All was silent now, save for the distant sound of the siren from Firth Brown, telling us all it was end of shift.

I shuffled back up the entry and through the back door, closing it securely behind me.

The dog was asleep in his tatty little basket and didn't even stir as I passed to go up the stairs and back to my bed.

***

The period between Christmas and New Year can, for some, be the most difficult, and sure enough, it was during this time that the depths of Peter's despair became apparent.

Like most of the neighbours I heard the ambulance long before I saw it, but I knew instinctively who it was for.

I ran towards Peter's house.

A small crowd had huddled at the bottom of the entry, and I pushed my way to the front.

50

A tall, thin-beaked copper was shouting, 'Get back! Let us do our job!' Then, 'I were supposed tu be off an' hour agu. Av got better things tu do, then tek some mong face tut nut house.'

Now that was fighting talk, and a mini riot may have ensued had it not been for the drama of a second ambulance arriving, this time at speed. So instead we stood in silence, hoping that all would be well, that this latest drama would be a minor misdemeanour, an injury-free non-event: shoplifting or something like that.

Unfortunately, our good wishes were dashed within moments, when Peter's mother was taken out and put into the ambulance. She looked tired and thin, her long grey hair was dishevelled. The food stains on the front of her pale-blue dress said it all.

All silent still, as two more medics ran up the entry with a stretcher and something strappy and white. I could hear shouting, but muffled, and then distant echoes of slamming and smashing and breaking, doors and pots and windows and pans, as out he came – out came Peter. He was strapped to the stretcher, restrained by a straitjacket, a gag shoved violently into his mouth, thrashing aimlessly, but still, unable to break himself free.

And as the back doors of the ambulance opened up, I stood in shock and sorrow as the tears welled, then fell, searing and stinging, onto my face. 'Peter!' I cried. 'Peter!' He was staring right at me, into my eyes. His, filled with fear and shame, silently pleading for my help. 'Leave him alone! Please, please, leave him alone!' I lunged forward, hurling a punch with my tiny fist at the rozzer blocking my way, but was quickly smacked back to the tarmac as the doors closed and the ambulance sped away, closely followed by its ridiculous escort.

Pub Watch was stumbling along the road, having just been ejected from what must have been a monster session at the Carlisle, the only pub that would still serve him. He was gesticulating at the Dibbles, flipping them the bird. 'Come on then, who is it? Who's the fuckin squealer? Who's bin fuckin squealin?' And then: 'Anyway I'm off … home an' tu bed … home an' tu bed wi fat fuckin Ada!' before falling arse over tit into what used to be Mrs Pepperdine's grate.

No one rushed to his aid. He could have stayed there for all we cared. We'd learnt from past experience that Pub Watch could win awards for skills to the Barnsley Kiss, planting one right between the eyes of anyone within striking distance. He was never grateful when it came to the kindness of others and so, silent once more, we stood and stared in a stunned disbelief as the convoy quickly disappeared from view.

**

After the Christmas holidays, Operation Bulldozer really started to take off. One day my friend Phosia was sitting next to me in class, the next she was gone, shipped off to some council estate on the other side of town.

Despite protestations, our happy little community was finally blown apart, as more families moved out, and more and more houses were EL-Offed and flattened.

It was strange living in a street where half the houses had been demolished. We were one of the last families to leave. Our faithful little house, with its mucky red door standing proud and defiant like a ruby in the dust, dwarfed by ghostly piles of bricks and rubble reminiscent of scenes from the blitz, memories of friends made, friends loved, friends lost and gone forever.

I was almost twelve years old, and by September would be leaving my middle school for a comprehensive, grown-up almost, so was surprised to see Evelynne waiting for me outside the school gates that January evening. She hadn't collected me since the day I'd left the juniors – something was wrong. 'What are you doing here?' I asked, searching her face for a clue.

'Thought I'd walk you home tonight, that's all.'

But I could tell by her expression that all was not well as we continued down the hill and onto the corner where the wool shop once stood. 'Clare.' Her face was serious and still. 'I've got something to tell you, but I don't want you to worry.' She took a breath and squeezed my hand tight. 'The thing is … the thing is … It's Peter.'

'Yes, I know,' I said, thinking her ambulance news slightly out of date. 'I saw him.'

'You saw him?' She seemed concerned, shocked almost.

'Yes, the time he was taken away. He was scared and he wanted them to let go, but they wouldn't, they wouldn't let him go.'

The memory of that dreadful day still haunted me, and my bottom lip started to wobble. But Evelynne was a pragmatist and all for the straight-talking, although always very careful with the delivery. So, placing her arm around my shoulders, returned to her main point, in a truthful, soft, motherly focus.

'Well,' she drew breath in and pushed breath out. 'Peter was poorly, and on Monday night he got so poorly, that he … I'm sorry, baby, but he died.'

I stopped in my tracks and, turning to face her, screamed 'Poorly? *Poorly?*'

'Yes, baby. He was very poorly and now he's not suffering – not any more.' Her words were stumbling. She looked scared.

I thought about it. What did she mean *suffering*? 'No, he was alright. I saw him … on Christmas Eve … I saw him. He was nipping my nose, and calling me names and he …' I put my hands over my face.

'I know, but sometimes people get sick very, very, quickly. And sometimes, they get so sick that they just can't get themselves better, no matter how hard they try.' I could see she was really struggling now. She loved Peter too, and this was hard for her. I wanted to ask more but, falling into her arms, had decided to swallow my words instead.

'I'm really sorry for you, Clare. I know he was your friend.' She gave me a cuddle. 'Would you like me to take you to the Wembley? We can sit on the swings and watch the snow fall down. I think it might land tonight.'

'Yes, please. I don't want to go back just yet.'

The playground hadn't yet been flattened, although it was just a matter of time, so we sat on the swings for a good hour, before finally deciding to set off for home. The snow had fallen soft and thick, just as Evelynne predicted, and was heavy underfoot as we silently left, still holding hands.

Turning onto what was left of Thorndon Road, we came upon the pile of rubble where Peter's house had once stood, and I felt the familiar ache of pain rising in my chest once more. This was bad, really bad: not just for Peter and his mother, but bad for me. I was really going to miss his all-kinds-of music, his hand-knitted tanks and his grey nylon shopper. The sunny days, the melted tar, the happy, sad, sometimes mad conversations, with my kind, witty, wobbly faced friend. My beautiful friend. Peter.

After being taken from the only home he'd ever known, Peter was placed in a secure mental institution and, no longer allowed contact with his beloved mother, became more and more distressed.

Following an assessment by some well-meaning, but unenlightened doctors, Peter was labelled 'mentally incompetent', and told that he'd have to stay in the care of the hospital for the rest of his life.

Terrified and unable to bear the pain of separation from both mother and community, Peter escaped the institution to which he'd been committed, via an open window in the corridor, just off the day room. And, taking himself to a nearby railway bridge, waited in the cold January air before throwing himself in front of a high-speed train.

Peter had a life, and we were part of it until slum-clearance bulldozed its way in, slapped us with an eviction notice and separated us all for good.

There was no doubt that his mother would have needed to go into a rest home at some stage; that she would most certainly have died before her son. In that situation we would have rallied – his friends, the people that loved him, the community, all of us would have rallied. In that situation he wasn't alone, he was one of us. But the community was no more. We were no more: like a vanished world, extinct and gone forever.

As for Peter, his life did not end on that cold January night: he'd died many weeks before, the day he'd been labelled, the day he felt different and plugged into the wrong socket.

Tracey Big Arms

The following September I moved from a small house to a big school.

Everyone else had taken their chances, running the gauntlet at the local comp, but Evelynne, being ahead of her time and having committed some nifty catchment area fraud, had managed to get me into Firth Park, which was considered the less delinquent of the two.

I realised on my very first day, however, that she may well have been punching above my weight.

Sitting in the assembly hall waiting for my name to be called was terrifying. All the other kids seem to know each other; they all seemed so clean and well dressed, unlike me, in a very ill-fitting uniform bought from Banners, a bargain-basement department store favoured by low-income families, pensioners and those bereft of any sense of fashion whatsoever.

'You'll grow into it,' Evelynne had said, as she pulled the enormous waistline of the skirt towards her. 'Just roll it over a couple of times. No one will notice. Besides, this lovely jumper'll cover it.' And with that, thrust a huge synthetic navy jumper into my hands, so big it would probably have covered the Horn of Africa. I looked at it and started to cry.

'Come on,' she rallied. 'We can't afford to keep buying uniforms all the time, and you *will* grow into it.'

Yes, thought I, if at some stage I manage to magically morph into Hellcat Haggerty, Dick the Bruiser, Billy Two Rivers, or just the combined Body Mass Index of all flipping three. Seriously, even the entire cast of Demis Roussos – The Movie, weren't *growing* into this get-up.

But it wasn't just the uniform that set me out as different as I sat in roll call that day – it was being skinny, having red hair and freckles, a crap school bag and the forty-denier ecru tights bought from the Co-op with two books of stamps. I felt marginalised, like a little ginger fish out of water and, for the very first time in my life, less than everyone else.

That said, the fit and feel of my low-cost attire was going to be the very least of my worries, because unbeknown to me, Tracey Big Arms was also joining Firth Park that day.

***

Tracey Big Arms was a loud and proud, overweight, tit-bitch, hard-faced and the wrong side of plain. She had all the signs and symptoms of a classic bully, in that she could not bear to be ignored.

Tracey was an abuser and, like most abusers, emotionally damaged herself. She hadn't known her true biological father. He'd abandoned her mother during pregnancy, leaving both to the care of a battered wives' hostel.

Her stepfather, a gentle, hard-working man, had doted on Tracey from the day they'd met, trying in his own way to right the wrong by working long hard hours to get her all the things her calcified little heart had desired.

But the benign parenting only made her headstrong and angry. No matter how bad the language or the behaviour, her parents showed no other reaction than that of passive goodness: no expression of disappointment. She'd never been challenged or disciplined in any way; she was, in short, out of control.

Now, every school bully needs an accomplice, and Katie Cat Piss (face of rat and 'Eau' of Cat) was to Big Arms'. Well, I say *accomplice*. Big Arms had total control over the Piss, who revelled in the attention, having never really been noticed before their alliance. She too now enjoyed standing out, as together they systematically terrorised an entire generation of second-year girls.

And yet, it wasn't until a most scandalous incident – involving a crash mat and a group of fourth-year boys – that the hefty stick of corporal punishment finally intervened, and Tracey's mother, a very glamorous coiffured woman, was summoned by the headmaster to discuss how, going forward, she intended to stop her wayward daughter being fingered in the gym at lunchtimes.

Neither party was the slightest bit interested in what the driver for such behaviour might be, or why she was so over-sexed at such a young age. This was the 1970s and psychology hadn't really been invented. No, the mother and the headmaster were meeting to discuss what the appropriate punishment for a 'misdemeanour' such as this might be: that was the one and only thing on the agenda that day. And, quite frankly, one hundred lines of 'I must not suck cock in the gym at lunchtime' wasn't exactly going to cut it. To expel her would be playing right into her hands, so the only thing for it was to keep her in at break and lunchtimes, thereby avoiding any risk of male contact: separation equals castration, or something like that.

Needless to say, my now overused terror antenna meant that I managed to avoid Big Arms and Cat Piss most of the time, except of course during PE, when we all took lessons together.

I loved PE and tried at all costs to avoid looking in their direction. Save for the fact that Big Arms appeared to have pubes like fuse wire, I hadn't so much as glanced at her sideways. I was still finding it difficult managing my father's mood swings, and although his job kept him away from home three nights a week, for the other four I did my level best to avoid him by joining most of the afterschool clubs. From gymnastics to trampoline, rounders to art, netball to drama, I was addicted to all. But it was athletics that really saved my life.

The physical pain of training seemed to counter the pain eating away at me on the inside, and the tunnel-vision mindset taught me how to compartmentalise – by staying in my lane and focusing on the win. Of course, the more I won, the more my father liked me and, spinning ever faster on the hamster wheel of affection, I soon became the son my father never had as, vicariously, he began to relive his lost athletic ambitions through me, even swerving the pub now and again to watch me race.

However, the attention I got on the sports field had firmly tubed me into the Big Arms' periscope, a move that was never going to end well. I was her polar opposite. She was big, blonde, privileged and spoilt. I was thin, gin, bargain and basement. She was never going to understand someone like me, so rather than try, decided to bully instead.

She began by chipping away with the things she'd say, picking me off and separating me from the herd. I was a freak, out on my own, primed for the bounce and, because of the post-match name-calling, really started to dread PE. But my athletic success was the only thing that had called a cessation to the torment suffered at the hands of my father. When it came to who was the biggest twat, he won hands down. So, despite an overwhelming urge to smash her teeth down the back of her throat with my short-distance spikes, I took an early decision to let it go. And, of course, life went on, with the names, the sniggers, the pushes and the shoves – the hate and the bile of the teenage bullies.

***

The lunchtime bell was already ringing as I walked down the corridor and into the toilets. A small crowd of girls had gathered at the mirrors, spritzing Farrah-Fawcett flicks firmly into place with large cans of ozone-no-object hairspray, shortening their skirts and fattening out uncrested school ties. The stifling smell of bootleg Charlie (perfume, not drug) and burnt spam-fritters hung heavy in the air.

I was sitting on the toilet staring down at my half-price shoes, wishing they were different, when I was sure I heard the cackle of a Katie Cat Piss.

The clamour of glamour, now afraid of attracting any unwanted attention, quickly left, taking their make-up bags with them, as through the silence I heard it once more: 'She's in that one. No, that one!' I knew instantly they were looking for me. I'd quite forgotten that Big Arms was out of quarantine after Cock-Sucking Gate, and free to roam the school again. They must have seen me walking down the corridor and followed me in. Why had I failed to update? This truly was a heart-sinking moment. Speaking of which, I couldn't hear anything apart from my heart now, which for some mad reason, appeared to be pumping in the back of my throat as, too dehydrated to squeeze a tear from a duct, I stood and reached for the Izal.

Okay, now I'd got it. It was coming from the toilet right next door. They were up to something. I wasn't sure what, until, 'Rag man! Rag man !' I recognised the voice – 'twas Big Arms. She was referring to my clothes. 'Bet you're not even on the rag yet.' Now she was referring to my skinny, prepubescent body. Her mouth was the most disgusting part of her whole being, and rendered a tirade of vile, abusive, no-holds-barred name-calling.

'No rags today? ... No? Well, have mine then!'

That was it. I knew I couldn't stay toilet-bound forever, and they weren't leaving any time soon. I had to get out. So, placing my hand on the cold metal lock, I slowly started to turn, when something warm, wet, and slightly greasy, hit me on the side of my face, at which point, the laughter, now directly outside the door, roared in volume.

'That's it!' I screamed. *'That is it!'* I opened up to a smug-faced Big Arms blocking my way, like some squat Benny Hill tribute act, her peevish little eyes two slits in her big fat rosy face.

I lunged my way out and, feeling the rage of an escaped lunatic, pushed my hand into her sniggering gob, ramming her through a cubicle door, smashing her oversized head on the undersized bowl. I fell in after her and grabbed her by the throat, whacking her hard, smack bang between the eyes, at which point her nose split open like an overcooked sausage, and the blood splatted down her triple-titted shirt.

Suddenly, I came to my senses and, realising that I might actually kill her, took a step back.

My head was thumping, this time with adrenalin that felt strong and powerful. True, I was still shaking, but in a good way. Then, moving ever so slowly away, I left her fat body wedged between the giddy delights of a bandaged-up old waste pipe and a begrimed toilet wall, swallowing the pain and seeing the sparkles, in a fetid pool of noxious splodge.

'Look what you've done!' screamed the Piss. 'Just look what you've done!'

I turned to face her, trying really hard to maintain some sort of dignity, which was quite difficult, given that I had someone else's period on my face. 'What *I've* done?'

She pushed me aside, scuttling to the aid of her friend. 'Yes, you! You've bloody well broke her nose!'

'Yes, and I'll bloody well break yours if you don't shut your bony neck!' Still refusing to back down, while at the same time attempting to clean my face with the sleeve of my Land of the Giants jumper.

'You'll get expelled for this!' she spat.

'Really? Well, in that case I think it might be worth it.'

I looked back at Big Arms, and the collapsed left nostril of her recent feature reassignment, as the panic and fear of the damage I'd caused began to seep its way into my psyche. *I could get expelled for this and, besides all that, what the hell was I doing?*

The one thing I'd learnt from the violence meted out by my father (the Emeritus Professor of Shite), is that nothing good ever came of it. Not just in the ticking time bomb of its emotional wounds, but in the corrosive fallout, the constant tit for tatting, the anger, the bitterness, the spite and revenge.

This time however, there was no revenge, no come back, no smart-arse remark. She just got herself up, walked over to the sinks and began washing the blood from her face with a rough green paper towel. In this moment she wasn't a monster, just a thirteen-year-old girl with a busted nose and a busted ego to match. Her bottom lip started to tremble as she studied the damage in the mirror. 'You didn't have to hit me so hard,' she said.

'And you didn't have to make my life so hard, either.'

'It's a laugh!' piped up the Piss. 'We were having a laugh!'

'Well, I'm not a joke! So find another!' I wasn't about to avoid the confrontation, and now she knew it, as she retreated to the aid of her friend once more.

I stood rooted to the floor, waiting for some sort of closure, permission to leave or just a kick in the face ... maybe? ... But still ... nothing.

So I pulled a green paper towel from the dispenser, walked over to the sinks and, running some hot water, began washing my hands, my face and the remnants of her disgusting missile from my hair. Tucking my shirt back into my skirt, I fattened out my uncrested school tie, face checked the mirror, and left.

I hadn't enjoyed hurting Big Arms in such a violent way. I was not a violent person. However, like most children living with a delinquent parent I'd become hyper-alert to the emotions of those around me. I had a heightened sense of vigilance to what I perceived as a threat, sometimes when there was no threat there at all.

Making the distinction had always been hard and, while knowing when to avoid confrontation is of course crucial, sometimes we have no other option but to start punching back, in order to put an end to those intolerable situations that can never be left to continue.

I never wanted to cause injury or harm, but the bullying had to stop.

The Big Arms fight was a good fight.

Budgies' Heads

If there was ever a year I'd choose to forget, 1979 has to be it.

In 1979 Dolly got married – to a woman – and if that wasn't depressing enough, had also secured full-time employment on the cold-meat counter of his local Liptons, where he was proving to be quite a hit, slicing corned beef into pensioners' portions, with a sharp repartee and the odd Bonny Tyler classic.

Although our friendship had waned somewhat post slum-clearance, the grapevine informed me that his new bride bore a striking resemblance to the incomparable Steve Davis, and his Catholic parents were beyond happy that their non-conformist son had, at long last, settled into conformity.

But Dolly was courting danger, and this had disaster written all over it. Women were not his thing, particularly women who looked like men. He was a runaway train going the wrong way down a one-way track. Someone was definitely going to get hurt, and it definitely wasn't going to be Dolly.

No, this time I wasn't wasting my worry on Dolly. The *annus horrbilis* of 1979 started for me with the death of my Granddad.

He'd been suffering with pains in his right leg, and only when it became unbearable did he call in the doctor. The upshot was that Granddad had a severe case of hardening of the arteries, caused by years of heavy smoking, and as a result the blood flow to his right leg had become hindered, which in turn had caused gangrene to set in. So, in February he was admitted to the Northern General for two operations: the first, an attempt to get the blood circulating again; and the second – a last resort – amputation of his leg, if plan A were to fail.

Plan A did, in fact, fail, and so my poor old Granddad William had his right leg amputated. Unfortunately, his heart, which had also been weakened by years of smoking, could not withstand the strain of two huge operations within such a short period of time, and early one morning he died, leaving Evelynne alone, and struggling to cope with the crippling pain of unbearable grief.

Although she was devastated, Evelynne stayed silent throughout. I'm sure now she was just being strong in order to protect the rest of us from what she knew would surely come.

Because my father, of course, was not quite so selfless and, at a point in our lives when we needed a 'Dad', he decided instead to revert back to type, by detaching himself from the pain of his kids.

Elizabeth, who was pregnant, had left home the year before to live with a man he hadn't approved of. Not only that, but Frances had also taken the chance to escape, when she ran off with a man twice her age. Needless to say, the Control-Freak-in-Chief took a zero-tolerance approach to both, and after cutting them off without another word began throwing himself around the house in bouts of drunken rage, not caring who he was hurting, and even less about the pain he was inflicting on Evelynne, who'd just lost her everything – the only man she'd ever loved.

With both sisters sent to Coventry and a funeral on the way, the atmosphere at home was dark and depressing.

I really disliked him during this fragile period of my life. I was grieving too, but when he turned his anger on Granddad's little black dog, I honestly thought I'd never forgive him.

Granddad loved KitKat, a scruffy, uncombed mixed-breed mutt, faithful, loyal and eager to please. He was his Velcro brother from a four-legged mother and they went everywhere together: to the bookies where Granddad had a part-time job, and Kit sat next to him all day long watching diligently as the odds were chalked onto the board; and then, later, to the Corner Pin for a well-deserved dust-settler, before taking the short walk home together for tea. They were entwined and, like two best friends, could not bear to be parted. So, when Granddad William died, his little black dog was racked with grief, frightened, confused and excruciatingly vulnerable.

On this particular night, just like every other really, my father came home from the pub. Of course, he didn't do vulnerable, and as usual was shouting up a storm. 'Shut it! Shurrup you stupid dog! Stop whining! Or trust me, I'll give you summat to really whine about!'

There was a crash and a bang, and then I heard the yelping. So I shot out of bed and ran downstairs headlong into the chaos, just in time to catch my father raining blows on the little black dog. 'Stop it!' I screamed. 'Stop it!' But he grabbed me by the hair and dragged me to the floor, before snatching the dog by the scruff of his neck, and kicking him, hard, into the cold, rainy, night.

I ran after out him but, bolting to the darkness, injured, terrified, lost and alone, KitKat had already disappeared. Granddad had got him as a puppy when I was five years old and now he was gone and, just like every other victim of my father's pathetic bullying, jettisoned without a second thought.

Week in, week out, I searched and searched, but it was to no avail. He'd gone for good.

I despised my father: he really was a careless, helpless, little man. To have been so jealous and threatened by a little black dog was beyond idiotic, the very height of stupidity. His low-empathic approach to parenting had made me insecure to the point where now I was finding it hard to function. I couldn't concentrate at school, so I left in July of that year with very few qualifications.

Constantly firefighting and tap-dancing to the tune of my father's stupid demands meant that I developed a real lack of sympathy for myself, as slowly but surely I slipped further and further into a big black hole, a big black hole of teenage depression.

With no words to describe the way I was feeling, I started to believe there was some sort of deficit in me. So I decoupled from normal life, shut myself down, withdrew and retreated into a bunker of shame. I didn't leave the house unless I absolutely had to, and lost contact with my friends who, unsurprisingly, found my behaviour intensely bewildering and hurtful.

Did my father love me? I wasn't really sure. It felt like a no, but in the absence of an answer to that question I blamed myself, assumed it was all my fault, that I'd done something wrong, that I was the bad person, unworthy of his love.

Of course, the truth of it was that I wasn't bad: I was a victim; a victim struggling in the shadows of my father's chronic self-absorption, and he wasn't changing any time soon.

Day after day, week after week, I slid further and further down, crippled by anxiety, fear and low self-esteem. I took the scissors to my hair, cutting off my beautiful red locks. I thought I'd feel something, but I didn't. I wanted to hurt myself, but in the end, couldn't even provoke a response. Like a corpse on a mortuary slab, everything about me was dead.

Too exhausted to function, I'd stay in bed ... sometimes for days. I didn't eat, I didn't speak, not even to Evelynne, who was so dreadfully worried. Even so, I hadn't noticed her pain; it hadn't even registered in my slow-moving psyche.

From spring through to winter my opaque existence continued. There had been much darkness, but slowly and surely some fleeting moments of light, moments when I knew instinctively that if I were to survive, to get back into the real world of people and life, I would have to disengage from my father, look upon him as just another person, depersonalise his behaviour and finally let him go. It was either that or start reading 'How to Kill Yourself' books.

The little black dog had been the very last straw. My father's approval was something I no longer sought nor required. If I was ever going to get through this (whatever *this* was) I needed a purpose in life, something to take me out of the house, under the radar and out of his way. Right now what I needed – really needed – was a job.

I knew on paper I was on the back foot, so I did two training schemes in an attempt to obtain some sort of skill. I may have been low on qualifications, but had the ability to keep going in the face of defeat, something that would allow me to move forward, make my own money and become independent, rather than constantly trying to placate my father.

I really didn't want to inherit his self-pitying approach to life. I wanted to make my own life, on my own terms. Yes, I definitely needed a job.

***

In 1980, a divorce-pending Dolly finally waved a fond 'au revoir' to the north of England, in pursuit of his new project: Roland, an extremely affluent but aged London banker, who he loved 'just for himself'. This was more like it: now he really was playing to type and would, no doubt, remain in character for the duration of the bonus.

Things were definitely looking up for me too, having finally managed to secure an income stream of my own when I started work at the National Coal Board.

I liked working. Much of my self-esteem now appeared to be tied up in my ability to work, so my confidence returned and, as predicted, my life started to improve in many other ways.

Although things between me and my father had also improved, I knew the ceasefire wasn't ever going to be a permanent thing.

The Tories had come to power in the previous year, bringing with them the first British woman Prime Minister, Margaret Thatcher. My father, a member of the Labour Party and not a fan of her pussy-bow politics, hated her. He said she was 'The hardest thing to have hit the working classes since rickets', and to be fair, he did have a point.

The steel industry had been the first to feel her wrath, and as a result my father was made redundant, never to work again.

It was around this time I started to notice the empty gin bottles next to his armchair.

No longer restricted to pub opening, he was now drinking post-pub through to the early hours of the morning, the acceleration from dependency to alcoholism in just the few short months following Granddad's death and his own unemployment.

There was something about alcohol that made him feel different, something that numbed his pain, but pain is a way of telling you there's something wrong and numbing is not without payback. My father was an alcoholic, and alcoholism is a progressive disease, a type of suicide. It was blatantly clear that he needed help, someone to stand up and say 'Stop!' But no one did. Not one of us attempted to halt his disease: we were too terrified to speak out, and he, in turn, would have become angry, defensive, hateful and ugly. Besides, I'd taken the decision to avoid his disappointment at all costs, and if he wasn't taking responsibility for it, then neither was I, and so, on it went.

I tolerated my father's alcoholism because it was better for me that I did. I closed my eyes and swallowed it down, finally deciding to file it in a box – a box labelled 'Budgies' Heads' – and move on.

Too Close You Burn

It was 1983. Kajagoogoo were number one, Keith Deller (138) a World Champion and my long, scrunch-dried spiral perm beyond fabulous. I was also in possession of a good job, my own money, a dazzling collection of ra-ra skirts and a sunbed tan the shade of a Clacton sunset. Yes, in 1983 I was definitely giving the ball a kick.

I wasn't on the hunt for him, but 1983 is when I met him, the good-looking, stomach-churning, final piece of the jigsaw – Mr Shagworthy, aka Tony Walker.

He was twenty-one years old, very tall, very dark and incredibly handsome. His thick collar-length hair framed a beautiful heart-shaped face, and a fantastical pair of pale-blue eyes sat, simmering sex, under what can only be described as a home-made fringe.

He wasn't really my type, not that I had one. In fact, come to think of it, up until then, the only man I'd ever really been mad about was Bernie Clifton, so I did sort of know that I was probably fighting science the very first time we met. He was wearing the most ridiculous pair of white round-toed shoes, teamed with green army-standard trousers and an Orange Juice 'Rip it Up' T-shirt, which for someone as fickle as me would have been an immediate packing offence under normal circumstances. Plus, he was a student. Previous to this encounter, I'd always viewed students as militant lefties with nut allergies, cabbage pants, roadkill hair and swing bins full of lentil-based leftovers that had been rotting for at least two months. So in retrospect, I must have had some sort of selective perception thing going on that night, and decided that his ability to make me feel like the entire contents of my stomach were being forced down my left nostril far outweighed his dubious sense of dress.

He was, in short, a heterosexual Code Red, and I wasn't about to fill out the forms and get in the queue. Patience had never been my forte, so over the next few days, I took the decisive action of turning the flirtathon up to full power, luring Tony Walker, his balding shoes, pop T-shirt and power fringe into the baited trap of my saucy little snare, unaware that he'd just tripped the wire and from here on in there'd be no going back.

Yes, this was speed-dating 1980s-style, and during one of my investigative conversations (some may refer to it as cross-examination), he told me that he quite liked the natural-looking woman. So, I spent two hours in make-up every day, trying to get the look just right.

Of course, it wasn't all about looks, these things rarely are: he was a very deep well and I knew I was going to have to swing this one on personality. Plus, he liked to read, and read a lot – a lot of hardcore literature. I needed backup, and decided early doors to bring out the big guns: Gunter Grass, Jean-Paul Sartre and Italo Calvino (whose *If on a Winter's Night a Traveller* I'd had to read at least thirty times before grasping, and to be honest, even then …) were just a few of the weapons in my turbo-charged arsenal of books. I also began to show more than a passing interest in rock-climbing, his sport of choice. There really was no length to which I wouldn't go, no river too deep, no mountain too high … and all that shit.

Just like Brando, I was in the 'method', and the poor defenceless heart-faced fool was falling for it, hook, line and gold-plated sinker.

That summer we walked for miles and miles up Wincobank Hill, holding hands as we lay on the ridge looking up at the stars or down to the tiny terraced houses below, their lights shining yellow and gold as the sky grew navy and dark. I'd never met anyone quite like Tony before, he was altogether very moreish. I was so in love I wanted a barrel of him and his ironic fashion, so when university was finally done, we decided to co-habit in a low-cost conversion at the other, more 'urban', end of Pitsmoor.

My father, of course, vented his disapproval in the usual way by cutting me off without another word – the ceasefire had, as predicted, ceased.

***

But living in bedsit land was tricky.

Having finally given up his full-time hobby of eating Ginger Nuts, Tony had found a job he quite liked working with computers, and although I was still working too, there was nothing going on but the rent. So rather than throw good money after bad we decided to cut our losses and try to buy instead. In addition to the difficulties surrounding the throbbing cost of living, there was also the issue of the psycho-neighbour factor swaying the popular vote.

The pimps and drug dealers that hung around the street corners and in the all-night cafés hadn't phased us. After all, we weren't really in the market for blow jobs or class A drugs, so were unlikely to have contact with them on any business level. No, in the end, it was the growing level of violence aimed at the ordinary that finally forced us to exit Dodge.

That and the fact that we'd been burgled by the most desperate burglars in the world, who'd smashed and grabbed everything we owned. Really, everything: from the kettle that wasn't electric, to the jewellery that wasn't real; from the alarm clock that never worked, to the fruit bowl that obviously did. They stole clothes, shoes, the iron, four packets of biscuits, three kitchen cannisters, two potpourris and a puzzling, if not indeterminable, amount of knickers from the dirty laundry basket.

Also, and shortly after that, the girl next door was savagely tortured by her boyfriend (also her pimp). He tied her to the bedpost and put a blowtorch to her chest until she finally admitted to the crime of sleeping with his brother – off the clock, of course.

'Quite frankly,' I said, packing a very small box with what was left of our belongings, 'I'd have confessed to sleeping with the dog if it meant hanging on to my nipples.'

'Too right,' said Tony, unravelling the knots in his climbing rope. 'Nobody likes a crozzled nozzle. Although, I still think the dirty knickers were by far the most valuable commodity down at the Albion car boot that night.' He was, of course, very left-handed.

***

In 1986 we were married (quite unceremoniously) at the registry office, with just two witnesses: Evelynne and another. We didn't have the money for a proper wedding, and besides, my father still wasn't speaking, so there seemed no point in making an event of it. And just a few weeks later, we moved, to the other side of town.

Our two-bedroom semi was a complete contrast to the Pitsmoor bedsit, and as the weeks turned to months, I slowly began to nest. Life did not exist outside mixer taps and I certainly had no interest whatsoever in anything to do with a career. I kept working to support my husband, who was by now my main focus in life.

Tony, on the other hand, was riding high. The company he worked for had offered him a partnership. So, I worked as much overtime as was physically possible to get the money we so desperately needed for the buy-in.

This was our new beginning and we worked hard to get the details of the brand just right. Our business plan included everything from fiscal strategy to corporate colours. We even had mugs and T-shirts printed in an agreed format that were to be rolled out once we were established, as slowly but surely the beast that was 'Rotherham Computers' (yes, I know, but it's all relative) grew, and with it my husband's ego, by now the size of a small planet. He was dressing well, in shirts I'd spent hours ironing. Looking handsome in clothes and hair designed and directed by his stylist – me. I invested all my time and energy in him, like some over-giving, caretaking idiot, with no sense of proportion or control.

I had noticed that other women found my husband attractive, but had always believed the years of scrimping and saving, the difficulties and the bad times, had somehow fused us, and that flimsy, self-serving relationships were for other people, not us. No, nothing was going to break us, certainly nothing as ridiculous as another woman.

As it happens, not everyone got that memo, and when I'd been admitted to hospital for an operation to remove a cyst from my ovary, I began to see things from a very different perspective.

A fat girl's one.

I'd put on weight as a result of my illness and subsequent recovery, which had also made me tired, dull and uninteresting. I really started to feel quite unworthy as one half of a relationship that had begun to spiral out of my control. I was becoming so needy I was almost mentally ill, and that's when things changed.

In August 1989, with enough jelly to run a Sunday school picnic, and hitting a massive 'Woah, Fatty' on the scales, I received a letter from some woman, informing me that Tony was having an affair. The letter had been written in the third person, but I knew instinctively that it was from the bastard adulteress herself.

Dear Clair

I have to tell you that Tony is having an affair with a beautiful girl, who has fallen so deeply in love ...

I'd opened the envelope, but not expected *this*! In fact, what was this? What did it mean? 'Beautiful?' and 'Girl?' What the fuck was this? I dropped it on the floor and walked into the kitchen, leaning on the worktop, staring down into the white plastic sink that I'd just Jiffed the fuckery out of a few minutes earlier.

Then, shaken and confused, I went back to the hall, and stared at the letter still lying on the carpet of our new house: the house we'd just bought; the house that had four bedrooms, two en suites, a dining room, three toilets (all cleaned and bleached), fitted carpets (Shake n' Vac-ed most days), and an integral garage, with room for two cars, even though I couldn't drive. *So what the fuck was this?* I put my hand onto my freshly stitched scar. I felt fat, frumpy and invisible. Then, falling to my knees, I picked up the letter and continued to read.

I don't want to tell you her name. She'd be devastated if she knew I'd written to you ...

That's when I *knew* it was the mistress; the sisterhood doesn't extend to girlfriends breaking news to wives about girlfriends being beautiful girls. No, this was the fucking home-breaker herself and, although I knew there was a basic truth to this, it had elements of the lying bastard about it: the affair might be true, the disguised first person singular was not.

The letter informed me that a beautiful girl (as yet nameless) was in love with my husband and he with her. The only thing standing in the way was me (the fat wife).

Perhaps girlfriend could appeal to my softer side and ask if I wouldn't mind flushing my life down the crapper by sliding back and giving in to the love, with a view to pissing off permanently, of course?

Could I? … Could I? … No, I didn't think I could, not yet. I wasn't going anywhere yet … well, not without some sort of exit strategy, that is.

***

That night all was still as my husband returned to Walker Towers at 9.30 p.m. Nothing moving save for my big fat punctured heart, beating slowly and determinedly in the back of my throat, beating so flipping hard, I thought I was going to choke.

I was sitting quietly in the front room listening to *Love Not Money*, which was a bit of a clue to my mindset.

'Hi!' he called, stepping through the back door, closing it with a slam.

'Hi,' I whispered, my voice as broken as my heart.

'What *are* you listening to?' he mused, picking up the album sleeve and studying it half-heartedly. 'Wow, haven't heard this in ages.'

I couldn't even look at him. The bitter sting of trampled-wife tears had welled, blurring my vision and choking my words. 'I'm reading *Will There Really Be a Morning*, and 'Ugly Little Dreams' makes it all fit into place.'

I felt his puzzled look, as he rolled his eyes and breathed a sigh.

'Tutting!' I screamed. 'Are you actually fucking tutting at me now?' I stood up, the letter screwed up tight, thrusting out my fist and dropping it at his feet.

'What's this?' he asked, bending to pick it up.

'Read it! Fucking well read it!'

In that moment, I wanted to kick him really hard in the face: his smug face; his beautiful face; the face I loved.

He prised the letter from its ball and began to read. And then, with a smile fading, smirk sliding expression said, 'Fat fucking Pat! Seriously, she's completely off her head.' He looked right at me. 'Come on,' he scoffed. 'You don't believe it, do you?'

I took a step back, trying really hard to reason things out in my spinning little head. 'Fat Pat?' Incredulous at the suggestion.

'Yeah, fucking shit up is what she does best. Ignore it, I'll sort it tomorrow …' And walked back into the kitchen with such an air of conviction that I was almost sold – almost, but sadly not quite … not really.

Fat Pat was a woman he worked with. He'd always said she had a thing for him, but I'd never met her, mainly because he'd never invited me to any of the parties they had at work.

I'd been banned from all official business functions ever since the night I'd tried to run a dinner for Tony and his 'associates' at our new house.

I'd been so overwhelmed with the responsibility of cooking nibbles of garlic chicken, which, as the night went on, looked more and more like stuffed vaginas, that to offset my obvious embarrassment and stiffen my ardour, I'd drunk a few too many vodka tonics.

After several trips to the loo, I'd made the genuine error of failing to fasten the poppers in the gusset of my all-in-one underwear (and let's face it, who hasn't been there?), leaving me waltzing around the front room with a tray of hors d'oeuvres and an extra-absorbent panty liner flapping defiantly behind me like some fifteen-tog flag, surrendering my complete inability to get anything right. So you see, I didn't know if Fat Pat existed or not, and mini chicken fillets have scared me shitless ever since.

Still, I was suffering emotionally; anxious and avoiding the obvious. So, for the next few weeks, I filtered out what I wanted to believe – and Fat Pat was it.

However, *Slagatha* wasn't about to give up, and by the time the second and final letter arrived, I knew I'd have to face the truth of my husband's affair, take it head on and deal with it once and for all.

As usual, Tony wasn't at home and I'd come back to an empty house to find the letter sitting on the hallway carpet, defying me to open it.

Dear Clair

Now, I can tell you, her name is Gail. They met at work and …

It went on about the nights out, the sex they had in the afternoon (at her house), all that, and still, *she's a beautiful girl …*

I stared down to the mean, scrawling writing, my name spelt

incorrectly with an 'i' and no 'e' – Clair. I really hated that she was quite prepared to destroy my life, but couldn't even get my name right.

At that moment the phone started to ring.

'Hello?' My voice was breaking again. Why couldn't I control it? Why?

'Is that Clare?' quizzed a woman; a woman, not a girl.

'Who is this?'

'Did you get my letter?' she asked, giving nothing away.

I felt the tremble of utter rage so, rather than demanding an answer to my first question, 'Yes,' was my reply.

'He's a bastard, Clare!' And with that, the phone went dead.

I put the receiver down and walked into the front room, falling back onto the sofa as the last seven years of my pathetic life flashed before my eyes.

Rain fell against the windowpane, the kind of rain that only falls in England late into the summer; that sweet-smelling August rain born from cloudy skies, softly washing away the dust of the day.

I sat, the tears now pouring from exhausted eyes, my whole body trembling with the slow hard boil of loathing and revolt, still clinging to the letter that was so tightly crumpled in my hand my fingers were losing their colour, turning purple, then blue and then … and then … I let it go.

Rising to my feet, I could see the man across the street returning home from work in his bright red car, locking it with a click, before opening his front door and going inside where his wife and children were waiting for him. I felt a pain that engulfed me into such a void of shame and abandonment. I hated my husband.

Here was I, winning the award for the longest time it took for the penny to drop, and no one to present it. The fucking lying bastard had let me believe that it was all crap – Fat Pat crap – when all the time, for the past three weeks he … he had … I wanted to start running, run out into the rainy streets, never stop, never come back. But then again, what I needed more was to smash him really hard in his arrogant, slut-shagging face, and kick *Gail* really hard in her big, fat, negligent fanny.

I ran upstairs and opened his wardrobe, pulling out his clothes: his suits I'd taken religiously to the cleaners; his shirts ironed by me, while he was being blown off by Bucket Fanny; his shoes – brown shoes, black shoes, all slung out of the bedroom window, into the rain and onto the lawn.

I went back downstairs and saw his stupid guitar, the one he couldn't even play. It was casually propped against the dining-room table. So, I opened the front door and 'casually' threw it into the garden, which by now was covered with the entire contents of his wardrobe.

Right, into the garage where he lovingly stowed all his climbing gear. Did he ever go climbing? Or was he just up Mount Gail? Well, in the absence of an answer to that question, out it went with the rest of his phoney life.

By the time Tony arrived home, the lights were on, the windows open wide and 'Total Control' by The Motels had been playing on repeat at full blast for the last hour. So, when the neighbours dared to glance over to see what was happening, it didn't exactly take the brain of Bamber Gascoigne to work it on out.

Upon entering the back door, my twat of a husband wore the expression of an incontinent boxer about to enter the ring without his padded knickers. He knew the game was up; it was just a matter of getting his story right as to how much of his life he could retrieve. So, I sat him down and told him in a very controlled way that I'd received another letter and a phone call from his mistress, Gail. And that, after a very frank and open dialogue, she had indeed fessed-up to the fact that she'd been sitting on his face till his nose bled for the last few months.

Of course, nothing of the sort had happened, but you really did have to get up with the sparrow's fart if you wanted to catch me out when I was in the mood.

'Well, okay,' he conceded. 'I have been seeing her, but it's not just a fling.'

At which point, the blood vessel in my right eye began to bulge and burst, but still he continued. 'I've had a crush on her for months and we went for lunch and things got a bit out of hand. Then, walking in Stanage Edge, I … I wanted to show her the things that—'

He stopped dead, and could no doubt see from the expression on my face that my heart, like his stupid old unplayed guitar, had been smashed to pieces, as the tears began to flood down my cheeks and into my mouth.

Stanage Edge was where I'd gone climbing with him when we'd first got together. I hated climbing – it was usually cold, wet and boring – but I'd wanted to be part of whatever he was, and so wind, rain, cold hard rock, I'd sucked it up, all of it.

I put my hands over my face. 'Right, that's it! That's enough! I don't need to know any more. Too much of an overshare with the walking-talking shit.' Sinking further and further into the sofa.

He looked at me now with a different expression, like all the weight of secrecy had been lifted from his lying mouth. His confidence returned, he did what all cheating men do sooner or later – he blamed his wife.

'Well, what the fuck do you expect? You don't care how you look any more. You don't wear make-up. You cry and run around after me like some demented fucking mother. You're twenty-six, not sixty! And I don't want to spend the rest of my life with a boring fat twat like you! How d'you think it makes me feel when I have to introduce *you* as my wife? How?' His accusing eyes were black and mean.

'Well, if you didn't go around launching yourself onto the nearest vagina, calling me fat, and claiming it's all my fault, then maybe I wouldn't want to eat so much fucking cake!'

I do realise how ridiculous that sounds, but there was a scary truth about it. If he hadn't made me feel less, I wouldn't have started acting less, and so on and so forth.

The tears that had been so flowingly thick were now starting to dry. So finally, he'd let it go: the truth of his frustration about my weight gain; my wifeliness that he'd grown to hate; and the imbalance that had occurred in our relationship as a result. Yes, he'd said it – it was all my fault. And yet there was more.

'I can't do this any more! I just can't! I want to be with Gail, she's everything you're not!' And, turning to leave, he got as far as the kitchen door before the flying teapot hit him smack bang on the back of his big fat head. I thought I'd kill him, but instead, sinking to my knees, begged him not to go.

'Why don't you get it?' he screamed, pulling me up by the collar of my plus-size shirt. 'It's finished! Get up! Get some fucking pride!' Then, shoving me back, back down to zero, finally made his escape.

I ran after him and, pulling the wedding ring from my finger, threw it down the garden path, screaming, 'Give that to Bucket Fanny! She can wear it through her fucking nose!' as off he sped in his big daft car.

Stumbling back into the house, I collapsed onto the kitchen floor and cried myself to sleep, not waking until the early hours, with the hexagonal honeycombed pattern of lino tattooed deep into my face.

***

I'd always had trouble keeping a situation right-sized, and so in the immediate aftermath of my husband's departure I'd not eaten, not slept, not washed, not done anything at all, save for rocking, crying and flinging myself around the front room like a demented chihuahua with a knit one, purl two, hand-knitted hair style.

As I became more and more disabled, my sister had no choice but to call in the doctor, a very small, well-meaning man, who visited me at home. He said, 'Break-ups are like bereavements, except that the other person is still alive, although not living in *your* life any more.' And, 'There really is no right or wrong way to feel in a situation like this, Clare. Just know, you are correct at all times.'

I gave him a vacant stare as I mulled over which Christmas cracker he'd pulled that punchy little pellet from and, of course, he had no meaningful response when, through a tear-stained face, I mumbled low and hard: 'I think I would have preferred it if my husband had died, and if I ever have the misfortune to set eyes on him again, I may well have to smash him in the head with the climbing axe he left in the garage.'

After a long silence, staring down at his scuffed, overworked doctor shoes, he hit me with another sparkler: 'You know, Clare, life is a series of mistakes, and we all make them – me, you, your husband – but we all learn from the experiences they create.'

He searched my face for some sort of acceptance, but I really wasn't up for the spewing platitudes or the emotional judo in the state I was in: it had A & E written all over it.

So, I politely asked him to leave, and reluctantly he did.

I sat on the sofa in the front room staring at the fireplace, its pale-grey marble backdrop and the white ornate plastered surround that we had chosen together … and started to cry.

Nothing sucked like this. Anyone who comes out with the 'It's better to have loved and lost' shit, has clearly never been kicked in the crack. No, nothing chaffed more than the pain of being fucked-over for someone else. Really … nothing.

I started to seriously believe it was me, my fault; from set off no one had ever stayed. My mother had left, my father didn't even acknowledge my existence, and now my husband was doing both. Had I made an endless series of mistakes, or just the one? Was loving someone more than I loved myself the biggest mistake I'd ever made? I'd put my husband first, his career, his wants, his needs. I had swallowed my career, my wants, my needs, to be his wife and it hadn't been enough for the bloodsucking self-centred bastard. He'd cast me off, like a worn out Widow Twankey from some mad pantomime in which his new love took centre stage like a shiny pink fairy, elevating him to a higher self. No, seriously, nothing, not even death, could have been worse than this kind of shit, especially for a pan-collecting, tap-polishing emotional outpatient like me.

Eventually, however, once the fog of oestrogen had finally cleared, the self-harming had run its course, and I literally had no more tears to cry, I began to enter the manic phase of a break-up, which mainly involved rage-cleaning the house in an attempt to remove every last trace of my husband out and into the garage, working through the night in my quest to erase him from my life and into brown cardboard boxes where he fucking well belonged.

Finally, exhausted, I decided that the only way I was going to get over the pain I was feeling (which by now was a physical thing) was to at least try to move on in some way.

I hadn't had any contact with my husband since the night he'd followed his cock to a greener pasture, and was still so emotionally attached to every word he'd said, over-analysing it time and time again, that to have another conversation would have been the very worst thing to have done, it would have put me under; for now, distance and detachment were best. So, after being housebound for two weeks, I finally decided to go back to work. Getting up really early in the mornings and having a sense of purpose not only diverted thoughts of turning up at my husband's office and macheting him and his mistress to death, but kept me busy and focused, as slowly but surely I began to recover.

All this wailing was such a waste of me, and I really did deserve so much more, so, accepting reality (but not defeat) I decided to hit the gym.

Exercise had always been my saviour. It helped me look good physically, but mentally it was my cure, and after a couple of weeks of some hardcore circuit training I was beginning to feel calm and clear, getting home so exhausted that I actually began to sleep at night, without waking once to worry or cry for my errant, slut-shagging husband.

Not only was I looking better, slimmer, toned, fitter, I also had a new group of friends and interests separate from the car crash that had become my marriage, and the further I stepped away from it, the more I realised what a total waste of time the last seven years had been.

And that's when it hit me.

I no longer wanted to be married: it had been one huge mistake. My father was, in fact, right: I should never have let it happen. I'd been infatuated with something that appeared perfect. Stepping out of the bubble meant the infatuation was over. So I put my marriage into a box – a box labelled 'fuck-up' – and decided to move on.

Too Remote You Freeze

Walking out of the huge glass doors of my solicitor's office, I felt the sun streaming through clouds onto my face, and for the first time in weeks the freedom I knew would surely come.

My lawyer, a very thin, short-haired woman, came carefully dressed in black, like some mark of respect for the death of my marriage. Her name was Ruth, and Ruth was the perfect man for the job: all about the business, but still able to grasp the weight of heartache I'd endured, when she said, 'I'll take this away and when it's all sorted, I'll bring it back in the form of a decree nisi, all neatly tied up in a pretty pink ribbon.'

'With a pretty pink fee note?' I queried, only half-joking.

'Yes. But you're too emotionally attached to think straight right now. I'm not. I can look at things in a more rational way, and as long as you don't contact your husband and start agreeing to silly things that best advice would frown upon, I'll keep it low. Fees don't have to be high for clients who do as they're told.'

I nodded in agreement. After all, you don't have a dog and bark yourself, and she was a bit of a pit bull, something I found quite attractive, even though, at that point, the latent lesbian hadn't quite kicked in.

The plan was that a letter would leave Growler & Co. by close of play the following night (Thursday) and would arrive at my husband's new home (Bucket Fanny Heights) on the Friday morning, giving him the weekend to fret himself bonkers about it.

Sitting on the bus, I reflected upon my current position and decided that the two main weapons in any good defence had to be access and timing.

Remove direct access from any heartbreaking twat, and any confidence of control they thought they had soon begins to fade. Their position becomes weak because absence forces them to confront their feelings rather than directing the blame your way, whereas constant contact gives them more hooks on which to hang the blame. In this respect, never confuse intimacy with proximity.

The timing of any notice of divorce should always be made through an officer of the court. Never threaten or shoot that particular bullet from your own hip, always let a lawyer get between you and a knee-jerk reaction. This not only says, 'Suck it up, adulterer', but adds a weight of seriousness that no amount of snot and screaming can: like taking someone to the cleaners on the golden service, if you will.

Feeling very pleased with my afternoon's work and having the next day off to hit Mad Julie's Phenomenal Abdominals, I went home, to wait for the sunbed I'd hired to arrive (I know, but it was the 1980s).

***

The curtains in the spare bedroom were closed tight, a precaution put in place to abate the pervy neighbour factor – the bloke across the road with the red car was conducting nightly in-house surveillance operations armed with heat-seeking binoculars, usually after dark, as his wife, exhausted by the nappy change and baby sick, slept on the sofa midway through *Coronation Street*.

I switched on my radio and, pulling the plastic goggles over my eyes, slid under the neon tubes hanging snugly over the bed. The fluorescent bulbs bathed my skin in warmth, and their slow faint hum lulled me softly to sleep, as just fifteen minutes on, I was jolted awake, when the timer clicked off with a buzz.

The radio was still in play and Morrissey was singing 'and pretty girls make graves' when I was sure I heard someone calling my name. I shot bolt up, smashing my face on the griddle and, still goggled, rolled out like an elite member of the Special Air Service onto the bedroom floor, scrambling for the plug.

Ripping both cap and goggles from my baking head, I clawed my dressing gown from the back of the door. And there it was again: 'Clare? Clare?'

'Who is it?' I called. 'Who's there?'

Silence.

So again, 'Hello?'

I could hear the familiar creak of the front room door and a

shuffling, unwanted presence in the hallway … And then … and then …
'Sorry, Clare, it's … it's me.'

Shit.

Motherfucker.

Fuck.

Shit.

I'd dreaded seeing my husband again. I'd worked so hard trying to get myself back onto my feet after he'd flattened me with his words and ground me to a pulp, stuck up his arse with the fat-wife speech, as I'd begged and pleaded for him not to go.

Seriously, it was enough to gag a maggot – I felt sick. Why now? Why come back now? In fact, why come back at all?

I stood behind the bedroom door with my face in my hands, then taking a deep breath in, slowly made my way into the bathroom, to put on some lipstick and pull myself together.

***

Now, there was no doubt that Tony was an intellectual, a well-read, articulate man, but really no match for me when it came to the linguistical gymnastics of arguing a point. I'd always been very good at arguing. In fact, I could have won awards for it. It was a naturally occurring talent, bequeathed to me by my father, a sergeant major in the Twat Army. In this instance, however, my tactics were to adopt an almost laissez-faire attitude: to smile and stay calm, keeping the hysterical side of my personality well and truly out of sight. That would put him off-guard, make him insecure and totally on the back foot.

So, with that in mind, I walked into the front room, to find him sitting on the sofa with his head in his hands. 'Hello,' I chirped, back in the game, with a confident swan. 'What brings you here?'

He looked up, physically recoiling at the sight of a size-eight me. I'd shed five stone in weight due to the heartbreak diet and, as a result of the over-exercising had the body of a fifteen-year-old Ukrainian gymnast.

'I … I … was … at a convention,' he stuttered, 'and coming back this way, so I thought I'd pop in and see how you're doing.' Incredulity in his eyes, as he continued to scan what was left of my body.

'Oh, okay.' But I wasn't buying it, the 'just passing' nonsense. I knew him well: he never 'just passed'. He wasn't a drop-in type, he always had to be invited; he was never spur of the moment. Even his mother had to give a twenty-eight-day pre-visit notice. 'Just passing' was code, a cry for help: something was wrong; something more had happened; he was all nods and smiles, a veritable smorgasbord of polite conversation, the polar opposite of our last meeting, when he'd been hard, calcified, hateful and ugly.

Since his departure, I'd fantasised about this moment many times – his return, the pleading to have me back, me doing the, 'It's not you, it's me' speech. That was how I'd imagined it and the feeling was supposed to be good. This, however, was not good. He looked tired and worn, like he'd been the injured party. He must have received Growler's pre-action letter, her hard, shiny words that said, 'There's no more bluffin' with my little muffin'. He must have, and it must have … hurt?

I sat on the sofa, proudly teasing the baby-soft curls of my new, post affair, 'fuck you' hairstyle, patiently waiting for him to squeak, when eventually … 'I got the letter from your solicitor.' Then, turning to face me, 'Is that what you really want?'

I stopped the hair-fluffing, trying desperately to suspend my own powers of credulity for a moment. Was that what I *really* want? Where did he get off? I'd been knocking out tears of dejection for weeks! What did he expect? Did he seriously think I was about to overlook Bucket Fanny Gate? Shrug it off, defibrillate my ailing marriage and take him back?

Really?

'Yes,' I smiled, still being a delight, not rising to the bait.

There was a heavy silence as he shifted uncomfortably in his seat. One minute, two, two minutes, three … and then, 'I was playing a tape you made me in the car,' he said, diverting a response. He was always such a subject-switcher, particularly when things weren't going his way.

'Which one?' I quizzed, deciding to go along with it. I'd made him hundreds of tapes for his car: music was our thing.

'The one with Patti Smith, Ivor Cutler and all that mad stuff you used to mash together.' He forced a smile but I knew exactly how he felt.

I hadn't been able to listen to music in the first few weeks of his leaving, switching off the radio as soon as the alarm kicked in.

Funny, how music will always do that. Just when you think you're safe, you turn on the radio and there it is, like a scalpel cutting straight to the truth, opening you up and laying you bare.

'You see,' he said, his eyes now starting to fill with what looked dangerously like tears, 'it hit me. Right then, it just hit me. I've fucked everything up, been a complete bastard. An' don't think for a second that I don't hate myself for it, because I do. But I don't want this to end. I want things to be the way they were … y'know the way they were before …'

So, there it was, right there on the sofa. Right there on the sofa with its head in its hands, that whingeing bleat of the false-hearted lover and the inevitable regret of their adulterous affair.

I couldn't decide whether to hug him or hit him. It was all so fucking disappointing: the last few weeks, the pain, the worry, and for what? A predictable U-turn, that for some reason was now my issue, a problem for me to deal with, and just when I was doing so well on my own.

I straightened myself up.

'Well,' I said, suppressing the urge to scream into a cushion, 'this is all very sudden. So you'll forgive me if I seen a little bit confused. But the last time I saw you, you were hiking up Mount Ego with a new love in tow, so what's changed?'

'I know, I know,' he mumbled without pause. 'I was a complete wanker.'

'You were, that. Then agen, you were in love … well, that's what you said.' My voice now developing a very unusual eight-octave range. 'So she must be happy. After all, she's got what she wants and without much resistance on my part, either. So now, y'can divorce me and marry …' I was just about to scream Bucket Fanny! I'd got so used to calling her that. 'So now y'can marry (*think, think*) … Gail.'

Yuck. The blandness of her name stuck right in my craw.

I sat back, shaking my head, waiting for some sort of a response, but he wore the expression of someone unable to defend himself: someone small, someone weak; it didn't seem like a fair fight. So I swallowed my anger – which, in truth, I had a right to – and shut up.

There was a long and drawn-out silence as he gazed at his shoes for what seemed like a fortnight: another annoying habit when he knew he was losing a fight.

Right then. Time to take a look, a really good look in a way that perhaps I hadn't done in years.

His thick black hair was clipped into a cool corporate crop and, although his image was much more styled these days, he was still, as they say in the tea rooms of Grimesthorpe, 'as fit as a five-mile fuck'.

But his beauty was a gift, natural and easy – he hadn't had to work at it like the rest of us do.

And there, I thought, lay the problem.

It must be hard being a captivator, the handsome, head-turning, headhunted, most wanted. I almost felt sorry for him – he was gorgeous and it wasn't his fault. But in a funny sort of way it was his weakness, and now, that weakness was mine.

I could see into the future, it was all mapped out: the years would pass, the lines would deepen, and he'd still be pulling focus.

Mount Gail was just the tip of the iceberg, a gateway affair, if you will. Because in five, ten, fifteen years' time, no longer a shagger-in-waiting, my upwardly-mobile husband was clearly set to be a full-weight serial adulterer. And yes, it was unfortunate, but with face like that, there was no future – he was not the man for me.

'Look,' he said, now letting out a shaky sigh. 'I don't want to fight. I just want to know how y'feel, y'know, how you *really* feel … about us?'

'How *I* feel? … Well, you fucked me over for someone else, so, I feel like that.'

'But, you can't honestly believe that I thought those things? Because I didn't. I was just trying to make you hate me, make it easier for you to … to let go.'

'Make it easier for *you*, y'mean.' Now he really was cruising for a punch in the pie hole.

'Trust me, there's nothing easy about any of this. Not for you, me, or Gail for that matter.'

Seriously, was he really trying to defend *her* now? After the way she'd manipulated and played him in the most single-minded deceitful way? You really did have to question his grasp on reality. What a glove puppet. It was official: I did feel sorry for him. He was clearly out of his depth, and from what I could see, in urgent need a better pair of crampons for the slippery slopes of the north face of Gail.

'Ah, come on,' I spat, 'you must have known she was the author of those ridiculous letters, making those absurd phone calls—'

'No, and stop being weird, why on earth would she want to do something like that? I mean, what the fuck's in it for her?'

I don't whether it was the look on his face, which was, quite frankly, ludicrous, or just the fact that by now I was borderline hysterical – I ripped a choke.

'Look,' he snarled, 'it was a mistake, just a stupid mistake and all I want now is for things to be the way they were. The way they were before ...'

But in truth, I had no more 'before' left in me, and he had no right to expect that I should.

In fact, if I stayed as a bit part in his extramarital future, I'd have to wave goodbye to who I really was, becoming insecure, mistrustful and nagging.

I didn't want to be that person, so I told him I had absolutely no intention of staying married to a man who thinks monogamy's a type of wood. 'Besides,' I said, now rising to my feet, 'I doubt I could manage the cystitis. And apart from all that, I've already filed you in the "fuck-up" box, and as you know, I don't conduct retrievals.'

Pot Noodle Sandwiches

I've always believed in my own agency, the ability to determine my own fate, which was probably just as well given the tsunami that became my divorce.

After creating my very own snowball of loveliness, I'd finally started to look forward to my future as an ex-wife (the title of choice): sexier than single, it had a feel of Barbarella-meets-Mrs-Robinson about it, even though I was only twenty-six at the time.

The financial shit, however, wasn't going quite so well, and was about to be blown wide open when, early one morning, a pie-fed fat bloke, with back jugs, breath like bus drivers' feet, and a thousand-yard stare banged on the front door.

'Mrs Walker?' He wore a full-length, black woollen coat, black leather gloves and had a flat, broad Yorkshire accent.

I thought he was either from the mob, or the TV Licensing office, so told I him I was the cat-sitter and that Mrs Walker wasn't home, that she'd gone off to Paris for the week and wasn't expected back until the following weekend.

He handed me some papers and told me to be sure to get *Mrs Walker* to call the number on the top of the first page. It was of the utmost urgency. If the amount outlined in red ink at the bottom wasn't paid within twenty-one days, then goods would be seized!

I took the paperwork from his fat little fist which, now ungloved, had the look of a trotter about it, and, closing the door open-mouthed, read down the list of 'creditors', which included: the mortgage company, the council for non-payment of council tax, the company we'd bought the car from, and a few store cards, all rolled up into one neat little document.

I recall that I had indeed received official-looking correspondence from certain parties, but had always forwarded them onto my husband, direct at his office, in an attempt to cause maximum embarrassment.

It was a Saturday morning. What was I going to do?

I knew I wasn't going to call Tony; men were useless in

situations like this. It needed to be dealt with effectively and within a certain timescale, neither of which were going to happen by getting Professor Ponderer from the University of 'I Dunno' involved. So, I got on the phone and rang round friends and work colleagues, explaining that I was getting a divorce … blah, blah, blah … that I had furniture, carpets and curtains for sale and, should they wish to purchase anything, to come over the following Saturday – cash only, no cheques.

By the time the bailiffs arrived twenty-one days later, the barrage of bargain-hunting locusts had already stripped the house of every cup, carpet and curtain in sight. The only items to survive the cull were a mattress on the floor that I slept on, a kettle (for the Pot Noodles), and a mug with the Rotherham Computers logo in green and white corporate colours – a cruel reminder of a previous life, a life now sold through the back door, before the bailiffs had even made it to the front.

Still, you can't dodge a debt forever, and a few weeks later I was summoned to court to clear the total amount, which now included administration costs, bailiff fees and something called 'accrued interest'.

This wasn't just debt, this was debt with a hard-on.

It was now glaringly obvious that we hadn't really been able to afford that life at all. It had all been one big illusion born from a combination of credit cards and bullshit. And now I'd gone over the fiscal cliff, along with my integrated appliances, Chinese sofas and chrome-plated mixer taps.

I sat myself down on the cold stone steps as the people in pinstripes continued to pass. I needed to think. Time was running, and nearly as fast as the flippin' interest. It was already too late to save my house: that was gone, gulped down the greedy throat of a shiny repossession order. Seriously, to have lost a husband, two en suites and a flat-screen TV was negligent enough, but to end up homeless …?

Fuck the grateful flow, thought I, as my tears began to dry. I needed to shake my monkey ass down to a mortgage company, and sharpish if I was going to prevent 'Living in a Box' becoming anthemic to my life.

I needed a broker, preferably vain and the right side of dumb, someone I could manipulate into giving me a mortgage before any of the court judgments were officially linked, knowing instinctively that once the list of debts had been registered, I was a marked woman.

To this end, I managed to secure a small mortgage on a tiny flat, after a short meeting with 'Financial Adviser' Matthew, a man so dull and lacking in self-awareness, he sought to boast that his previous occupation on the complaints counter at Radio Rentals had been a 'Life lesson in problem-solving'.

'You'll find,' he said, loosening the top button of his over-tight Ben Sherman, a small splatter of blood on the collar from that morning's hurried shave, 'nothing, and I mean nothing, gets past me, Clare.'

'I'll bet not,' agreed I, with a very broad, very confident smile.

***

Meanwhile, on the other side of Rotherham, my bankrupt husband, now unemployed and living with his mistress, was no longer such a catch either. The 'Funky Cold Medina' had definitely started to wane, as their relationship – which was always more pecuniary than passionate, like his one-dimensional business plan – began to implode.

Still, there was nothing one-dimensional about living in debt, or the miserable gaping hole of despair that its poverty creates. And six months on, as promised, the court was taking its monthly payback. I wasn't allowed a cheque book, cash card or credit of any kind, and could only make very limited withdrawals, which were monitored at each visit to the bank by the Nazi officers posing as cashiers.

Yep, I was finally living in that land known as 'out there' – single, but in desperate need of a double income. So I took a second job at the gym I'd joined a few months before and soon became an instructor, taking five classes a week, which helped to stave off some of the more extreme symptoms of my calamitous destitution.

Unfortunately, Britain was also sliding further and further into recession, and British Coal, that nationalised jewel in its once-glorious crown, slowly but surely began to contract and, as a result, I was given two choices – both quite stark.

The first: redundancy.

The second: to be demoralised and demoted to the position of a general dogsbody, and moved to the slavery of the Claims Department.

Of course, being up to my Jane Fonda G-string in debt, and just two short reps from losing my shit, I decided I'd opt for the latter.

***

I found the first few weeks in my new position emotionally quite hard: juggling the hardship at home, and starting again at the bottom of the British Coal food chain was unsettling at best.

The Claims Department was a huge open-plan office, with groups of people separated into teams. Each team had a leader, whose job it was to coach their squad through the processing of thousands of claims made by miners who'd had accidents or been made deaf as a result of working at the pit. It was a busy, fast-moving environment. Piles of claims files filled the desks of administration clerks, who busily tapped information into computer terminals.

I'd been allocated to work on the team that dealt with claimants who had the surnames A to F, and was instructed by *my* Team Leader, Gary – a man slimier than snot on a door knob – to start by sorting the post and pulling the files for the Claims Assessors and Administration Clerks.

'You've got to understand,' he announced, fixing his rat-boy eyes firmly between my legs, 'you've got such a lot to learn. We're here to defend claims. It's a very important job and you're going to have to learn every aspect of it – well, to a point – starting with the post.' He pointed to a huge red plastic pouch filled with letters, and continued. 'Grass roots, that's how I started, and who knows,' shrugging his bony shoulders, 'in a few years' time, you might get to be in charge of your own team. It's been a long hard slog, but hey, if I can do it …'

'Yeah,' I said, not realising I was talking out loud, 'I can't see Richard Branson trembling over his joss sticks just yet, can you?'

He shot me the look of someone who didn't have a sense of humour and, pausing for a moment to size up my tits, continued. 'Look, this is a *real* department, not some Mickey Mouse IT unit, like the one you're used to.'

I looked into his mean little eyes, framed by cheap, bendy, round-rimmed glasses, and sighed. 'Well, here's hoping I can master the alphabet, otherwise we're all shafted.'

He wasn't even smiling. 'You'd better sit across from me then, an' that way we can both make sure.'

I took my seat at the desk opposite and he handed me a huge pile of post. 'Sort it into alphabetical order and get back to me,' he snapped.

What a complete wanker, thought I, still managing to smile nicely. I really disliked everything about him, from the ridiculous ponytail he'd managed to scrape from the remnants of his very thin, very wispy hair, right down to his bootlace tie and Joan Jett trousers. Some men were just not meant to go hell for leather, and Gary was one of them.

During my first few weeks I didn't really speak to anyone apart from Gary and the other people on my team, who, although quite nice, didn't appear to be offended by his casual misogyny and racist remarks in the same way I was. I cringed every time he opened his unenlightened beak and for the first time in a long time was beginning to feel quite depressed. I was going to have to tune Gary out, give him the budgie's head treatment, if I was going to keep my much-needed job, and that was a fact.

***

After a few weeks mastering the filing system and becoming a dab hand at stamping the post, I was eventually let loose on computer input. Having worked in IT previously, I was able to get through file input quickly and accurately but, needless to say, it was a very dull sticking plaster over a very septic career.

During my time at British Coal two things had become glaringly obvious: first, that all the top jobs were occupied by men; and second, that most of them had been in situ for at least one millennium, managing to stay ahead of the curve by taking what can only be described as a casual, non-committal approach to business development.

It was only when denationalisation came a-knocking that the senior management, who up until this point had been sleepwalking into the handover, suddenly realised that if we were going to be able to compete with other service providers and keep the claims-handling business, the curricula vitae of the job-for-life squad would require a serious review.

Adverts were posted on staff noticeboards and anyone interested in taking professional qualifications was invited to register that interest immediately.

I knew that I was capable of much more than the mundane administration I'd been limited to by Gary, who, after taking an instant dislike to me, had attempted to put me down at every available opportunity. In fact, I'd posted my own interest with HR that very day and was excited when I was given a time and date for interview.

I decided I needed to dust up my interview technique, so I drafted in my best friend and sounding board, Caroline, aka Psycho Cop.

Although Caroline was in possession of a vagina, she had all the feminine charm of a Sherman tank. She'd left home to join the army at just seventeen, before leaving to join the police (the force, not the group) when she was twenty-two.

I'd met her when she came to one of my sessions at West Street Workout, and damn near broke her legs in my Step class. She, in turn, had respected me for it, and nailed her colours to my friendship mast.

Caroline was bisexual and, having just come out of a long-term relationship with a girl in the army, had decided to try men for a while to see how that would fit. I'd always valued her opinion: she was matter-of-fact and straight to the point, never mincing her words or romantic in her delivery. So, when I met her for a chat and a sandwich at the cathedral I knew she'd give me an honest appraisal.

Always on time, she was sitting on a memorial bench, waiting for me in a navy-blue uniform complete with hat, eating what was left of a Marks & Spencer chicken and sweetcorn sandwich.

'Hello, missus,' she screeched.

'Hi, Caroline.' I kissed the top of her hat. 'Okay?'

'Yeah.' She rolled her eyes. 'Well, no. Bloody Morgan's been at me again.'

'Not again? Where this time? Not the charge office?'

'No, not at me as in the shagging sense, no.' She pointed straight at me. 'You!'

'But I thought we'd resolved this issue last week on the cheese counter at Sainsbury's.'

'I know, but he's not backing off just yet. He's been on nights this week and keeps turning up at my flat, which is bloody annoying, not to mention borderline stalk.'

Morgan was a married man working the same shift as Caroline, and she'd been having casual sex with him for some time. I'd met him on Saturday afternoon, when we bumped into him on the cheese counter at our local Sainsbury's. He'd been a sex pest then, asking me to 'Give me a call sometime', which I found odd, if not a little disloyal, given that his shagging buddy was my best friend and pushing the same shopping trolley at the time.

'I mean,' she said, taking one last bite of her sandwich, 'I could have been in all kinds of positions, with all kinds of people. And what about poor old Valda (her vibrator)? She's a very private person.'

'Exactly. And anyway, why turn up at the flat when you share a perfectly good panda car?'

'Clare, nobody calls them panda cars any more, you big Judith blouse.' She wasn't smiling.

'Well, what did he—?'

'A threesome,' she side-mouthed, cutting me off.

'With which combo?' I didn't need to ask, but my nerves were getting up.

'Two girls. He suggested his wife, but I don't really fancy her, so … so … I thought you might …?'

'Well, thank you for that, but there are three major impediments to that particular love tryst. First of all, I don't like vaginas; I find it hard enough dealing with my own, never mind anyone else's. Secondly, you're my best friend and, as much as I love you, I really don't want to eat your pussy. But again, thanks for the offer. And finally, Morgan is a lazy-eyed lunatic, who turns up at your flat in night-vision goggles on the off-chance of a free blow job, and has, from what I can gather, an IQ in single figures. I can't even begin to imagine him with a hard-on, much less being on the end of it!'

'Is that a no, then?' She looked at me, and started to laugh.

'No. It's a never.'

So, there we sat, until it was time to go: her to armed robberies and me to filing back. We agreed that the only way I was ever going to get my square peg out of the round hole that was Gary, was to get qualified and, with that in mind, I went to my interview with a renewed optimism after what had been a very dark and dismal twelve months of life.

***

The morning of my interview I was up early, my discursive mind having hindered my ability to sleep. I hadn't eaten very much either, I'd had to buy an electricity token and the £5 fee had wiped me out, save for the bus fare, which was higher up the list of priorities that day.

It was 10.30 a.m., and the phone on my desk started to ring.

'Hi, Clare. It's Marie, Malcolm Hutley's PA. Malc's asked if you wouldn't mind popping down now, please.'

'Yes, of course,' I shrieked, in what might have been an over-desperate tone. 'I'll come down immediately.'

Malcolm Hutley, 'Muttley' to his detractors, was the go-to man when it came to funding. He was stout, stumpy and bald of head, with a bright pink face and hands that trembled from the copious amounts of alcohol he consumed in the pub at lunchtimes. His bushy orange unibrow (the envy of many a self-respecting caterpillar, no doubt), was a defiant nod to a ginger past, dominating an otherwise globy, somewhat blindworm appearance.

Muttley was an over-grasping, tactless, greedy little man, who worked for his own benefit and exploited everyone else. You were either in Muttley's gang or you were out. Those in, were the men that would drink with him in the marathon after-work sessions and play golf to lose at weekends, or the women prepared to have his sex in that budget hotel on the dodgy side of town. I wasn't in either camp: I couldn't afford to eat, never mind drink, and I certainly didn't have the stomach for the sex thing. Speaking of which, my empty stomach was churning like a firkin as I nervously knocked and he asked me to 'Come!' He was sitting behind a light-tan Formica desk, in a big black leather chair, looking a bit

95

like the Wizard of Oz at the end of the film when the curtain falls back.

I was disappointed to see a smug, ponytailed Gary in the chair right next to him, wearing his navy-blue suit, a new purchase from Top Lad no doubt. I wasn't surprised he was there – disappointed, but not surprised. Let's face it, there are some people that can never really surprise you, and being a key member of the Muttley Posse, I knew Gary would see it as his mission to maintain my dust mite status.

I was in a no-win situation from set-off. Rat-boy Gary had given Muttley the Puce the lowdown, and unless I was prepared to be spit-roasted right there on the shiny Formica desk, any hopes of getting my study fees paid, were, as they say in Armthorpe, 'bolloxed'.

I don't know what it was about Gary. He always had the ability to stoke a non-specific anxiety in me. I couldn't see the point in him: he never made sense. But then again, thought I, silently clearing my throat, do I really need to understand Gary? After all, I'm not the Knobhead Whisperer.

'Please,' said Muttley, 'take a seat.' He pointed to the chair on the opposite side of the desk. 'Just so you know, Gary will be sitting in throughout, not just to observe, but to ask a few questions of his own should I fail in my duties.' They gave a laddish laugh. 'And who knows, he might even pull me up with a few pointers of his own.'

'Ha! Yes.' I over-smiled my agreement. 'Who knows?' And, turning to acknowledge him with a nod, said, 'Hi, Gary.' Who returned the nod without the greet.

Muttley shot me a puzzled look. 'Well, that's the icebreaker out of the way. Now, let's make a start.' He peered down at his A4 pad. 'So, tell me something about you, Clare. Let's start at the beginning. How long have you worked here?'

'For British Coal? About ten years or so.' Attempting a confident smile, while at the same time trying really hard not to hum the *Stop The Pigeon* theme tune or scream 'Muttley! Save me!' in a very ill-suited emotional-type moment.

'And how long on claims?' He hadn't appeared to notice.

'Erm, just a few months.' My nervousness starting to show.

'Why, can you tell us,' (they shot each other a 'you've been discussed' look) 'should we fund *your* studies, say, over those of one of your work colleagues, one that has, say, been on claims longer?'

I hadn't realised that there were only a set number of places available. Still, I didn't have to think too long to answer. 'I think it's important that money is spent wisely and in the right area. Funding should be given to those who are capable of completing the course and obtaining the qualification at the end of it. Just because you've worked in a department for a long time doesn't automatically mean you're capable of achieving – or are even committed to the goal of – professional qualifications, and I'm aware that's what we need in order to compete with other, similar organisations, whose staff *are* professionally qualified in law and insurance.'

Muttley's face softened. He liked what I was saying. I could see I'd pressed a button. I'd also pressed Gary's – his over-competitive button right in the middle of his mean little head. His face was like a busted clog. He wasn't happy as he sat bolt up and, with his size-nine leatherettes, started to stick the boot in.

'Well, you've answered your own question there, Clare.' His stare was fixed right at me. 'You're not exactly the brightest bulb in the tanning booth, if GCSE results are anything to go by.' He shot a knowing look over to Muttley's side of the desk and, with his spiteful little cat lips, continued. 'What evidence have *we* got that you're capable of achieving anything academically? Quite frankly, I'm surprised the Board took you on at all.'

I could feel the anger rising in the attractive crimson colour developing on my neck, always a giveaway when I was about to reload and blow. 'Well,' said I, trying to maintain an unaffected pose, 'before you start stomping those tiny Cuban heels, you appear to have ignored the fact that I remedied my lack of academic prowess with my O level achievements at Sheffield College, and the two work-experience courses I completed after leaving school. All undertaken in an effort to secure a position at British Coal – an industry I'd always had the ambition for.' I wasn't about to open up to rat-boy about the fact that my father was an abusive narcissistic twat, and that it was a miracle my sisters and I had even survived to school age, never mind passed bloody exams. No, this was no time for a Lassie speech.

'College, my arse! NVQ? What's that? I'll tell you what that is! It's an "I'm not very qualified and my name's Barbie!" That's what that is!' I stared, open-mouthed. It was official: he really had no filter and, apart from that, what the frigging heck was he banging on about? NVQs hadn't even been invented when I left school; come to think of it, neither had GCSEs. No, this really was too much. I'd spent months enduring the racist ramblings of 'Ger' as he now called himself, and the angry little ponytail he referred to as 'his look'. His nasty sense of humour that was always at the expense someone else; someone he'd deemed less than himself; someone weak.

The only way 'Ger' could inflate his ego was to undermine others. His sexist comments were incredibly tiresome and I'd put up with them for long enough. I'd always been verbally dexterous, but he'd never really felt the sharp edge of my tongue and now, for some mad reason, the urge to take him on overwhelmed me and the time to lacerate had finally arrived.

'I'm sorry, Gary, are you saying that I lack content? That I'm not robust? That I'm a bit … *fluffy*?'

With the comfort of knowing he'd flipped my anger switch he continued. 'Well, let's just say there's more to taking exams than jumping up and down off boxes.'

'Actually, there's more to teaching aerobics than jumping up and down off boxes, but I wouldn't expect a wig on a stick like you to understand that concept for a moment.'

His face dropped from smug to fury. Good – jam on. I'd just got going, and now he was going to get it. 'Where is it written that ugly little knobheads with a City and Guilds in Kerplunk, and passive-aggressive ponytails, have the monopoly on brains? Only, that maxim didn't appear to feature in the Welcome-to-Claims pack you gave me, *Ger*.'

Muttley drew breath as if to cut in, but Gary cut him off at the pass. 'I think we've made our decision, and it's a "No" to funding this time, Clare, but feel free to apply again, when hell freezes over, of course.'

Muttley was wearing an expression of concern and trying to

inject a sense of reason into the argument. Le Muttley was muttering, 'Let's try not to voice criticisms as personal attacks. It won't get us anywhere.' The jargonese of his low-grade management speak was one of the most irritating things about him: that, and his touchy-feely office politics. Even so, 'Going forward', 'reaching out' and 'at the end of the day' it was way too late for a Muttley 'blame-free rewind', so I shot him a look that said 'put a sock in it, or maybe just the barrel of a gun', and, taking the cue, he fell back to his seat.

Gary, realising that he may have gone a bit too far with the 'Barbie' comment, attempted to pull things back onto a more professional track. 'I agree with Malc. Your over-emotional personal attacks on me only confirm what we first thought – it's a definite "No" to funding, and what's more, I don't want you working on my team for a moment longer. So I'll suggest you're transferred with immediate effect.' He turned to Muttley. 'If that's okay with you, Malcolm?'

Successfully neutralised and still stuck to the back of his seat, Muttley nodded in silence.

'Well, thank you for that, Gary. Every cloud and all that. And thanks for your time: it's a beautiful thing when two become one.' I wiggled my index finger between the two of them in order to drive the message home, but Muttley wasn't making eye contact, so I rose to leave. 'Oh yes, and, Gary ... if we *are* judging books by covers, you should definitely take your act to Vegas. I hear ponytails and leather trousers are the very thing with magicians right now.' And with that, marched out, leaving the door wide open behind me.

What a result! No more Gary. Okay, I was going to have to fund myself through college – how, I wasn't altogether sure – but for now, no more Gary. This really was cause for celebration.

Right, thought I, trotting down the stairwell. *Mad Julie does it with weights, and a Pot Noodle sandwich for tea.*

***

However, that Saturday there was bad news from Frances.

Evelynne had been admitted to hospital as a result of a really bad fall.

A few days later, after installing a bed in the dining room as she could no longer climb the stairs, issuing a commode, a Zimmer frame and a few leaflets on how to handle getting old – *when your body has been mangled in an accident, but we can't let you have a bed, because the National Health Service is on its knees, even though you've paid in all your life* – Evelynne was sent home to be cared for by my father, who was happy to take the carer's allowance, but not to undertake any of the caring.

After a few weeks back home, Evelynne started to suffer from severe bouts of loneliness and depression. She'd taken to listening to talking books as her cataracts were getting so bad that she was unable to read or focus on the television, which was a constant source of frustration to her.

For my father, nothing changed: he continued his lunchtime drinking, then back to bed in the afternoon, only rising to scream abuse at Evelynne for daring to listen to her talking books and interrupting his hangover naps.

The food he bought was of the cheapest boil-in-the-bag variety. He didn't help her to eat, bathe or empty the commode. Instead she'd sit and wait for hours, for me and Frances to arrive. Poor Evelynne and her unconditional, love-driven, misguided loyalty.

But Frances had a plan.

She contacted social services and, on hearing her account, they agreed to visit Evelynne straightaway, taking all of fifteen minutes to confirm that she was indeed living in squalor, and that the situation was so serious that she had to be removed from the house immediately.

'Would you like to go into a rest home, Mrs Hinchliffe, just for a couple of weeks' respite?' The female social worker was amazingly good at tempering the relationship between Evelynne, my father and her care allowance.

'Oh, yes, luv, I would,' nodded Evelynne, eager to be saved.

'Well, alright. We'll get your granddaughters to pack a few things and we'll get you there today, if that's alright?'

Evelynne's face was a picture of relief. 'Thank you, luv, thank you.'

My father, still glued to his chair, had the face of thunder, but with no time to dwell, Frances and I ran upstairs to pack her bag, air-punching with glee that she'd finally been rescued, was finally safe.

After two weeks in the rest home, Evelynne had a visit from the same social workers, who told her that she really ought to consider becoming a permanent resident, something she'd prayed for and was more than content to do until … 'What about me? What's going happen to me then? I depend on that money! How am I gonna manage now?' My father's voice was controlled and every bit as scary.

Luckily, Frances and I were there for backup and had decided earlier that day that our sole mission was to ensure Evelynne stayed in care and wasn't sent home, to what would have surely been a certain death.

'Stop it!' spat Frances. 'Just stop it!' and I almost fainted.

No one had ever spoken to him like that before. I thought she'd be picking her teeth up with broken fingers as he shot her the death stare. But he gave no response, other than, 'I'm going outside for a fag!' as he rose to leave, still glaring – this time at me.

'No, Bill, don't worry,' cried Evelynne, getting more and more distressed. She reached into her cardigan, pulling a little red Post Office book out of her pocket, which contained her life savings. 'Here, Bill,' she said, holding it up for him to take. 'You can have it.' But Bill was a twat and, turning his back, decided to leave her hanging instead.

'Never mind that, Mrs Hinchliffe.' The social worker was getting her dander up too. 'What do *you* want in an ideal world?'

Evelynne put the little red book back into her pocket and, looking at me and Frances as the tears started to well in her pretty blue eyes, whispered, 'I want to stay.'

***

Over the next few weeks Evelynne's health began to rapidly improve. Her tidy little room was pretty and pink, with a matching planted pot that she called Ivy, perfectly placed in a pristine bay window, hogging its light from the gardens outside.

Of course, being a delight, she made lots of new friends. They sang songs, played dominoes and held whist drives – where residents could win boxes of chocolates, fruit in tins and hand-embroidered handkerchiefs – a pastime Evelynne loved, having been a regular at the whist drive throughout her pre-residential life.

It was a relief to see her so happy and relaxed, being her ever so beautiful self again. Her laughter, something I hadn't heard in such a long time, was back, as was the warmth of colour in her face and the twinkle in her pretty pale-blue eyes. Her clothes were clean and her hair perfectly set into soft, toffee-coloured curls, not a hint of grey to be found.

Visiting was altogether a much nicer experience. No more depressing house, or treading on eggshells, with the mood-swinger and his over-fragile ego telling us exactly what we thought and delivering judgement on every word we dared to utter. We sat at ease talking about the things that mattered to us, without fear of interruption or political objection – my father's presence was no longer sought, nor required, for that matter.

'Okay,' I said, rising from my position perched comfortably on the edge of her bed. 'I'll get off for the bus.'

'Alright, luv, thanks for coming.' She was dwarfed by the high-backed chair, upholstered in pale-pink velour, a perfect complement to the light, airy room. 'Ooh, now, before you gu, can you just get me two on them little sweets out for tomorrow?' She pointed to a jar full of multicoloured sweets.

'Just two?' I pulled at the lid.

'Yes, luv, just two. I like to have 'em wi mi books.'

'Right, two little sweets it is. Red an' a yellow alright?'

She gave me a nod, as I put them on the hand-crocheted doily next to her cassette player, ready for the next instalment of Daphne du Maurier.

'Now,' she said, with a natural concern, 'you get yourself off before it gets dark.'

Industrial Disease Barbie

A few weeks later, having been given the boot from Team Gary, I was transferred to a new team. This was the lead-in to the privatisation of the coal industry and I'd been selected to work on a pilot, set up to develop new working practices for the old British Coal regime, in an effort to get the organisation up to speed with the very competitive insurance market – a job that, quite frankly, no one else wanted.

My boss, a very serious, hard-working woman called Sarah, was the polar opposite to petty, office-tyrant Gary, who, after denying me access to educational funding, had managed to secure the funding for himself and his ridiculous girlfriend Suzi – a Pam-Ayres-meets-Timmy-Mallett-style fembot – who wore clogs, had chain-mail hair and laughed uncontrollably at everything, be it funny or not: a prerequisite, no doubt, for any brain donor taking on the social workout that was Gary.

Sarah, on the other hand, was a strong, intelligent, gifted human being, who after leaving Cambridge with a first in Law had, for some mad reason, accepted a job at British Coal, and because of her academic brilliance was the youngest person, not to mention only female, to have reached her level in the corporation at that time – hot on the heels of Muttley and his crew of corporate knobheads – the middle management menfolk, aka FOMTs (fat, overpaid, moaning twats) – who didn't want women muddying the waters of their domain, much less someone as scary as she was. They were secretly resentful, excluding her from set-off, making bad jokes about her gender, her weight and her total inability to take them seriously.

To them, she was the nutcracker, so they bitched behind her back, but never to her face. She terrified them, and what's more, she flipping well knew it. No, Sarah didn't want their good opinion, or anything else that was easily come by. She liked the feel of blood and sweat on her fingertips, the satisfaction of something earned the hard way, and had volunteered to set up a new team when Muttley had refused point-blank to get involved. He, like the rest of FOMTdom, was averse to change and, in any event, held the view that if it failed, she'd take the hit, fall flat on her face. After all, she had it coming, and let's face it, when the shit hits the air con, then deputy heads will roll.

***

Having put the dark days of Gary and his post stamp behind me, I took an early decision to work with Sarah and make this pilot rock, and from set-off we clicked. The Claims-Meister and her knacker-cracker-in-waiting were highly motivated and joined at the head (save for the fact that I didn't appear to have her control when it came to cake), and on this particular day, were enjoying a plasticated coffee from the free – but really crap – staff drinks machine. We had a powwow that afternoon and were getting all jacked up on caffeine-based beverages in readiness for the bun fight. 'Clare,' she said, 'can you get me the weekly reserves? I know we have them monthly, but I want you to start running them every week. Y'know what Muttley's like, and I'd rather be prepared than not.' She was leaning back in her swivel chair, craning for contact from behind the partition. We sat next to each other in the top corner of claims, but because she was important, she had a partition.

I rolled my eyes. 'Muttley, Muttley, dearest Muttley, the face that launched a thousand stats. Already on it.' I pointed to the shelf above her head. 'You'll find them in the red folder, the one entitled: "coefficient variations of a fat duck's arse".'

'Perfect,' she smirked, glancing at her watch as she swung on back.

At which point, tick turd Gary decided to swing on by, grasping a bacon sandwich in his anaemic little hand. It was dress-down Friday, and he was wearing his black 'Larry Laughter' T-shirt, the one with a list of tour dates on the back in white lettering, his stonewashed jeans, a throwback to the 1980s, as were his over-white, underused high-top trainers.

'Have you seen Suze?' He was constantly following her around the office, like a stalking weasel.

I looked up from my screen and noticed he'd started growing that knobby little ponytail again, the one that looked even more pathetic than the previous full-grown version. 'I think she might be in the toilet, powdering her brown nose.'

'Piss off!' he spat, heading for the stairwell.

'I'm sorry, Gary, are you talking to me, or just withholding educational funding?'

'Like I said, think of the rainforest, Barbs, an' don't waste the fuckin paper!' He gave me the finger before disappearing through the fire doors in hot pursuit of Sooooz.

I shook my head. 'It can't be easy having to wriggle under Captain Crap Fuck every night. I mean, even if she was totally blind, she can't have lost her sense of smell, or dignity, or both, can she?'

I looked at Sarah and she was laughing, which was rare; she didn't laugh very much at all. 'Being quick-witted,' she said, still scanning the stats, 'is a real sign of intelligence, and good claims people are multitalented and technically adept, just like you.' (That was the other thing, that I forgot to mention earlier: she spoke the truth at all times.) 'So why,' now staring right at me, 'aren't you studying your ACII?'

'It's not like I haven't tried,' I said, taking a sip of tepid Ajax with extra milk, 'I did apply. However, much to my dismay, Gary had already talked Muttley into rejecting my application after a hard day's arse-licking in the middle management wank parlour. So, given that, and the fact that the holes in my one and only pair of shoes are now padded out with cardboard,' I shoved my foot in her face, displaying the square of cornflake box holding my black suede slingbacks together, 'the £750 fee's not really a priority, but bus fare, my dear sensei, has to be!'

'Well,' she said, looking pityingly at my pathetic footwear, 'we'll bloody well see about that!'

***

Always as good as her word, Sarah had just one thing on the agenda at the next senior management meeting and, after securing funding from a reluctant Muttley, I started an after-work course in Insurance and Law.

I studied hard and had my head in my books at every available opportunity. I simply had to pass my exams: failure was not an option; there could be no slippage. Gary was also on the course and I had to wipe the smug look off his ratty little face and bury him in the academic graveyard – anything less would have been a total fail.

Also, and by now, the pilot was proving to be a huge success and soon began to grow, as more and more staff were drafted in to assist. Rather than having administration clerks carrying out the menial tasks of filing, looking for post and generally wiping the arses of the FOMTs, we implemented a new way of working whereby all staff, regardless of grade, were to handle their own claims, from cradle to grave, within a financial limit. This meant that the higher-value claims would be handled by the highly paid Claims Assessors, and the more straightforward, less-complicated cases would be handled by the more straightforward, less-complicated Claims Assistants, utilising a claims questionnaire completed by the Safety Office at the pit.

The aim was to reduce costs, utilise and train staff that had previously been an untapped resource, and make some kind of – dare I say it? Screw it, I'm going to – *profit*.

A move that kicked off a huge wave of resistance from the FOMTs, who quite enjoyed half-days at the pit taking statements, then taking off home on an early billet to watch *Countdown*. Not only that, but to add another massive insult to their very minor injuries, Barbie was promoted, too. Sarah, in her wisdom, had put me forward to become an assessor.

However, when I'd been given Wistow Colliery to investigate, the mentor earmarked to train me had flatly refused to do so. He was half-man, half-Siberian Hamster, and his name was Derek. 'The best thing you can do,' he snapped – dispensing advice from under a handlebar moustache that did nothing to disguise his inflated cheeks, or the huge gap between his front teeth, and only sought to enhance the general appearance of rodent – 'is try a spot of DIY an' do it your fucking self!' slamming a box laden with old outstanding investigations onto my desk. He wasn't looking at me, but at Sarah, who was sitting with her back to him, ignoring the protest.

As he flounced back to his messy desk, she freewheeled towards me. She was a pretty girl; her fine blonde hair was cut into a sharp businesslike bob, but her shoulders stuck out of the top of her shirt like two bread knives. She was very underweight, emaciated even, but something we never discussed. I did want to get close, find out what the hunger strike was about, but in the end just didn't have the nerve.

'Don't worry about that,' she said, with a side nod to Derek, the Captain Pugwash of Claims. 'You can drive, can't you?'

'Yes.' I couldn't.

'And have you got access to a car?'

'Of course.' I hadn't.

'Well, there you go. Get yourself booked out for your colliery visits. Call the Safety Officer at the pit and arrange a time to interview your witnesses. If you need help, I can always give you a hand when you get back to the office. But do it, Clare: don't give them the satisfaction of watching you fail, not now.'

That very night I went home and scoured the Yellow Pages until I found someone who ran a four-day intensive driving course with the test being on the fifth, deciding to miss a mortgage payment and pay the £400.00 upfront fee instead – needs must and all that. And my needs definitely *musted*; I literally could not afford the fail.

A fact immediately tattooed onto the forehead of my instructor, a very quiet, well-meaning little man, with a natty collection of suede-panelled cardigans and the patience of a saint, who, despite describing me as a 'worst-case scenario' had kept calm in the face of the most challenging of circumstances, and hadn't so much as blinked an eye when I'd almost taken out a bus queue of pensioners, after an oversteer on a sharp bend.

Needless to say, by the time my test came round, we were both ready to see the back of each other, and surprised and relieved in equal quantities when Tim the tester, with a face almost as green as his anorak, announced that I'd passed!

And a week later, bang on schedule, I was on the road to Wistow Colliery.

Hollywood Miners

Stepping out of my borrowed car, after a white-knuckle drive down the M1, vacuum-packed and ready to roll with a briefcase full of outstanding investigations, I felt like I'd truly arrived: a lone woman in the industrial world of man; a diamond in the coal; bold, confident and unafraid. What an agent for change I was in my tight little business suit and my high-heeled slingbacks, with the cardboard still holding them together.

I sought out the signs for the Safety Office as I made my way with ease through the heavy double doors into the main colliery building.

Passing the lamp room, where miners collect their check tags and safety equipment before going underground, I heard a shrill of wolf whistles coming from behind a filthy serving-hatched window. 'Alreight, luv?'

I couldn't really see the face. 'Yes, thanks.' I air-smiled.

'Need directions?'

'No, it's okay.' Maintaining my stride. 'I'm after the Safety Officer.'

'Eye, arn't we all?'

I don't know how many of them were in the lamp room at the time, but they all seemed quite happy to be there.

By now it was almost midday and I was there to interview witnesses to the claims Derek had passed on, many of which were really old and out of date. Pit accidents were all too common, and for every case settled another five would arrive in the post, so I was determined to clear the backlog as soon as I possibly could.

When a miner suffered an accident at work, an Accident Report Form was completed by the Shift Supervisor or Pit Deputy, giving basic details of how the accident happened.

These details, taken at the time, were crucial accounts of the facts, because as time passes memories fade and witnesses became unreliable. Sometimes, however, when more serious incidents occurred, the Surveyor's Office had to draw up more detailed accident-site plans. Going on from this, if a miner was referred to the colliery medical centre post-accident, there was usually a medical-centre record which set out further details of the injuries sustained and any treatment given.

Now, the biggest whinge of your average FOMT was that the Safety Office did not supply all the information they required within a reasonable time – untrue of course. As the indisputable Hong Kong Phooey of admin support, I knew exactly where the blame lay, and it wasn't with the people at the pit, who were never going to bend over backwards for those they'd been so alienated from, and deliver up information with a nice cup o' tea an' a large slice o' cake. No, if you wanted evidence, you had to go out there and get it. So, part of my charm offensive was to make contact with all surface officers and get a coordinated system going, whereby all information would be supplied in good detail and good time. Well, that was the plan, as I steamed down the corridor, with the raised voice of man still muffling over the tannoy.

Finally, I approached the Safety Office door and, with a sudden gush of panic, nervously knocked, as I stepped inside.

A slim man in dirty orange overalls, with ear defenders round his neck, was sitting behind a shabby wooden desk, leaning back into a filthy old chair that must have been a blue colour at some point in its life. To one side, a black push-button telephone sat high on a pile of old papers and site plans; a metal sandwich box with a Granny Smiths apple perched on top sat to the other. 'Hello!' he bellowed. 'You must be Clare Walker.'

'Yes. Paul?' (Well who else would it be? Idiot!)

'Eye, that's mi name, don't wear it out.' (Obviously thinking the same.)

'Erm, we spoke on the phone, I'm here to interview the witnesses to some accidents, and I …'

'This is Dave Parker.' He turned and introduced a short man, who was sitting on the windowsill in a pale-green nylon shirt, and a mauve tie with the NUM logo on it.

'Hello, luv.'

'Hello. Clare Walker.' I walked further in to shake his hand.

'Well,' said Paul, 'this is a bit of a turn up fot books – a female assessor. They'll be queuing tut canteen an' back for an interview wi

109

thee.'

'Eye, chuckin the sens ont panzers.' Dave joining the fun.

'Well, I certainly hope so!'

Silence. Now they just looked perplexed.

'Oh, no! Not the panzer thing. No, the queuing for interviews! I … I've got so many, it's making my head spin.'

'Well, that's why I wanted thee tu come in a bit early,' said Paul, tipping the nod in Dave's direction, a cue to a private discussion.

'Reight,' said Dave, taking the hint. 'I'll see thee around, luv.' He crossed the room and opened the door. 'Let mi know if there's owt tha needs.' Slamming it with a bang.

It was definitely shut now.

'Ny then,' said Paul, leaning further into his chair, 'all this bloody crap about Safety Officers sorting out them bloody questionnaires is getting me down, luv.'

'I know,' I nodded my agreement. Safety Officers were very busy people, and to load more and more work onto them didn't seem fair at all, given the idle twats that turned up for a couple of hours to investigate, throw their weight about, demand AR1s and site plans right, left and bloody-well centre. I was with him on this.

'Is there some way y'can help mi if I get snowed under?' He was trying to turn on a charm of sorts, but his brown teeth really let him down.

'Well,' I placed my battered briefcase onto the floor and sat myself down, 'as a matter of fact, I can.'

'Great,' relief in his face, 'because that bloke that's bin here fot last three years just turns up when he wants an' I don't see him from one shift tut next. Then he's off, an' if I want tu talk tu him, I av tu phone bloody office! Me!' He pointed to the top button of his overall, which was open revealing a gold belcher and a very mucky vest. '*I* av tu phone *him*!'

One thing worth pointing out is that Safety Officers are almost Crowned Heads of Europe status: you chase them; they do not chase you.

'Okay, well, what if I took them off you today and got them sorted, once an' for all?'

'All on 'em?' His mouth dropped open wide.

'Yes, all. It'll give me lots of practice, and if you're happy, you can sign them off.'

'Wey hey!' He air-punched. 'That's great!'

'But I do need a favour in return.'

'Oh, eye?' Suspicion in his tone.

'Yes, I need to make sure that I get all the site plans and med-centre entries exactly when I need them, because if I don't, and my investigations end up late, then Derek the Hamster and Gary the Stoat will trash me! And before you know it I'll be stamping the bloody post again!'

I could see by his face, Paul didn't have a clue who Derek and Gary were, but was trying very hard to understand. 'Okay, no problem. You tek mi questionnaires, bring 'em back when they're done, an' I'll check um an' sign 'em off. Leave it wi me. I'll get ault plans y'need. I'll also mek sure witnesses turn up an' don't just bog off hom wi'owt seeing you first. Don't worry, we'll work it together, an' you'll never stamp another envelope agen!' He started to laugh. His teeth really were the oddest shade of *greige*, but his face was kind and I liked him very much.

All interviews were to take place in the Safety Office and, as Paul left to go underground on inspections, I took my place behind his desk ready for my first miner to arrive.

Sited proudly on the wall directly in front of me was a dirty calendar, in which an attractive brunette had her tits out, advertising surface diggers, and the fact that it was April, should anyone be interested. Another, featuring a blonde wearing nothing but the safety helmet she was pushing to sale, sat above my head.

Aware that an open fanny can be quite distracting to the average man, I decided to place Post-its over her large knockers and gaping bush, and sat down, ready for battle.

My first interview was with a man called Vernon, a hairy-arsed Ripper built like a brick shithouse. I knew he'd arrived when he stood filling the door frame, shouting, 'It were a claim! Gerrit paid.'

'Well,' I said, 'if it's a genuine claim I'm sure it will be, just as long as you don't mind going through what happened first, of course.'

He threw his metal snap tin onto the desk, taking his place on the chair opposite, which buckled slightly, barely standing his weight. I wasn't quite sure if he'd come for an arm-wrestle or to answer my questions, which at this point in time did seem a little inappropriate, not to mention condescending, given his obvious air of authority.

'Okay, you're here for …?' I nervously checked my list.

'Paul Stokes. Brok his foot when a ring leg fell on it.'

I could tell he'd showered, but coal dust clings and was in evidence to the inner lids of his eyes, his ears and his fingernails as he swept his jet-black hair away from his face with hands like shovels and, leaning elbow to thigh, looked right at me.

'Okay, before all that, I'm just going to need a few basic details about you first. Then we can get into the circumstances surrounding the accident. Well, that's … erm … the order of it, anyway.' I shuffled my papers straight and, pen poised, squeezed him a smile.

He in turn rolled his eyes with an expression of 'boring twat' and, sighing a hefty 'Reight', finally gave in.

So I began.

'Okay, can you just confirm your name, address and check number?'

'What's *my* name?' Incredulous to the notion that I hadn't heard of the legend that was Vernon. 'It were a claim, gerrit paid!' He shot a puzzled look at the Post-its on the calendar. 'Vicarious liability! Eric dropped ring leg on Stokey's foot and brok it in half a dozen places.' And that was also the thing about miners: they were, to a man, expert in the law, swapping evidence over a pint in the Welfare like a set of barroom barristers, offering up advice on liability and quantum, on everything, from black fingernails, to post-traumatic stress. They knew their way around the personal injury circuit better than any high street solicitor. 'Tha dunt need tu know owt else other than that.' Still eyeballing.

I felt the freaking hackles rising on the back of my neck. He was really getting on my tit end now. 'Yes, well, like I just said, we'll get round to the circumstances surrounding the accident shortly. But for now, I'd really like your full name, address and check, and preferably before the night shift arrives!'

'*My* name?' He whispered, stroking his chin.

'Yes, *your* name.'

I started to tap the desk with my BIC, a sort of pre-fight war cry, as he sat bolt up, his eyes catching the calendar once more. 'Fanny! Fanny Tittensor.' And with that, started to snigger like an oversized idiotic schoolboy.

I threw down the pen and, emptying my lungs, let out a huge sigh. 'Well, how very apt, because from where I'm sat you do appear to be a bit of a c**t!' Then, realising what had just spewed from my mouth, looked round for a window to hurl myself out of, as I nervously waited for the kick-off.

Laughing, he fell back into his chair. 'That's a good un,' he said. 'I'll have tu remember that one!' He held out his hand. 'Vernon Green, and you are?'

'Clare, Clare Walker.'

'Squawker Walker! Hope tha not goin down pit wi that attitude! Thall scare 'em all to bleedin death!'

Vernon's knowledge of mining was second to none. He was an expert in systems of work and knew every roadway and drivage in the pit. He could relate any gradients or height restriction from pipe ranges and belts, he was a full-weight mining oracle. He told me that the men on his shift hadn't been given proper lifting equipment and had been left to drag ring legs up the face, on uneven ground, in restricted height and clearance. Paul Stokes had played football for the local village team and had been lucky not to have lost his foot when it was crushed in the accident.

'I dint want another Terry Braithwaite.' He shuddered. 'Cun't do that agen.'

I knew this case from the file papers in the office: the photographs were hideous.

Vernon had been the first on the scene to dig Terry out from the fall and, without care for his own safety, had tried desperately to save his life by administering mouth-to-mouth. But Terry had suffered fatal head injuries and, with his dying breath, had regurgitated into Vernon's. The sickening taste of his friend's last moments had touched his lips in a memory too dreadful to contemplate. He couldn't eat, he couldn't sleep, as over the days and weeks that followed the psychological effects of the accident took their toll on Vernon, who'd tried time and time again to make a better ending. But no matter how many times he replayed it, the outcome was always the same: Terry had died in the most hateful of circumstances, leaving Vernon to struggle with the ghost of that memory, the upsurge of grief, and the crippling symptoms of his post-traumatic stress.

Stoic by nature, Vernon chose not to seek assistance, medical or otherwise, continuing instead to work through the flashbacks and night sweats as best he could. But never to be undone was the emotional numbing that saw him unconsciously wringing his hands as he snapped himself back to the present. 'It's a long way tut surface when thas got thee foot hangin off. First aiders gen him morphine, an' I helped um carry him up an' out. He's bin off for twelve weeks already; lost his overtime an' his bonus. Nice lad is Paul; just a pup, really.' He shook his head and, picking up his snap tin, whispered, 'Can I gerroff now, luv?'

'Yes, thank you.' I smiled. 'That's been really helpful.'

Vernon was to be respected, and the claim was paid.

***

Week after week, I forged on. Underground, overground and sometimes even on the ground, in a one-woman, witness boot camp.

'Thad better tek thee mek-up off,' giggled Paul, as I left for the cage.

'Take it off? Don't be so ridiculous!'

'Thall regret it when tha comes back up!'

'I doubt that. Besides, glamour doesn't have a dimmer switch!'

He shook his head in comic disbelief. 'I dunt know about a chuffin dimmer switch. Thas gonna need some bloody paint stripper!'

'Yeah, right.' I threw him a nod and carried on my merry way. As far as I was concerned, eyelashes, lip gloss and loose powder aside, I was just like everyone else, handing my check to the Banksman in my helmet, overalls, gloves and boots – apart from the fact that the coal dust did, as Paul predicted, stick like glue to the Estée Lauder, making me the blackest in the cage. Still, there was no backing down, even when Industrial Disease Barbie had finally hit pit bottom.

'Can you swim? There's a lot o' watter dine ere today, luv,' came a shout from the Button Man, as I swung off the belt, which slowed, but funnily enough never seemed to stop – not for me, or the Headers who worked in their pants because of the heat that was constantly thrown out from the face end. They said if I was one of the team, I'd do the same.

'When I'm on fifty quid a shift like you lot I'll seriously consider it!' I squawked, and they heckled and jeered, but never once held the lack of a Y-chromosome against me. They were going with it. Then again, they'd the wrath of the canteen ladies to contend with, and there was no creature on the planet harder than a pit canteen lady – except of course, a miner's wife.

Yes, the 1990s designer miners liked to showcase their six-packs and tool belts, much to the dismay of the older pre-retirement generation, who'd worked hand-filling from the age of fourteen, and now worked pre-retirement light duties in the surface workshops or pithead baths. They called them 'the Hollywood Miners' because they'd swerve the Welfare in favour of a wine bar and a nightclub.

The Hollywood Miners – why shouldn't they have their fun? They'd worked hard for the pleasure in dust and danger, where serious accidents were commonplace. High on risk, low on fear, they were close-knit, protective and loyal, not just highly skilled in the job of mining, but also in their own emergency service. Your team was your family, and might well have to save your life one day. Vernon was right: it was a long way back to the shaft and hundreds of metres up to the surface. It was brave to be able to manage that kind of stress, and hard-working miners faced danger every day of their working lives. They expected claims people to know their stuff and if you didn't have mining sense, you were over within a moment. It was dog eat dog, and I wasn't about to start wearing marrowbone underwear, so I made it my mission to work with Paul and his team to ensure we offered a fair and comprehensive claims service to the men. I was never off-duty, working long hours by day and studying by night, passing my first year exams with distinction, and even winning the Institute's Student of the Year Award as a result.

***

Meanwhile, back on the barren wastelands of Planet Gary, bad news loomed heavy, like a thick winter fog. Despite an inflated sense of skill, Gary hadn't made the grade, and even after retakes hadn't managed to get one pass out of the twelve subjects in the module.

I wanted to say something smug, but honestly, felt quite sorry for him, so resisted any putdowns that might well have rolled from my tongue at one stage in our relationship. I'd never thought of Gary as human before; I always thought he'd been knitted, but there was something about his failure that had shouted out and shut me up.

He never made eye contact again, not even to mouth a silent, 'Fuck off, Barbie,' as was usual when we passed on the stairs. I almost felt bereft: he'd even jettisoned the gravedigger's ponytail in favour of a more contemporary look. Poor Gary. It was all true: he really was unhindered by talent of any kind, back in his unqualified box and licking his wounds, unable to face the failure.

Two Little Sweets

On a bright and shiny September day, while up to my neck in accident reports, the phone on my desk started to ring. 'Hello, Clare Walker.' Now my career was halfway on the move, I'd taken to announcing myself.

'Clare, it's me.' The prodigal pater? Blimey, I hadn't spoken to him in weeks, not since our Evelynne visiting times had clashed and he was en route to the Corner Pin. He never called me at work, or come to think of it, ever, so I knew something was wrong before he'd even started.

'Oh, hello, everything alright?'

'No, no, it's not.' A snappy, hard delivery as usual.

'Why? What's happened?'

'It's your nan. She's had a fall and they've taken her to the Northern General.'

Right. Evelynne had fallen before, the last having landed her in hospital and subsequently into care. I knew her fragile little body couldn't take another like that and started to panic. 'How did she—?'

'I'm not sure. Apparently she slipped getting out of bed an' they think she's broke her hip.'

'Have you called Frances?'

'Yes, but she's not picking up, an' I need a lift to the hospital. By't time I've got ont bus, it'll be time to come back, so you'll have to take me instead.'

'Okay, no worries. I'll be round at six, if that's alright?'

'Sounds like it'll have to be, dunt it?'

Here we go, why couldn't he just be nice, just for once? Why did even the simplest of discussions have turn into arguments?

'But I thought visiting was six till eight. If I get to you at six, we'll be there for quarter past.'

'Right.' Big tut; huge sigh. 'See you then, then.'

***

'Can you keep the meter running? I'm just going to get my dad, then we want to go to the Northern General.'

'Okay, luv,' said the driver, reaching for a flask, and that night's edition of *The Star*. 'No rush.'

I slammed the door a bit too hard getting out of the cab and ran to the front door of my father's house, giving it a furious knock with both fists. It was bang on six, not yet dark, but for some mad reason the lights were on and blazing through open curtains as I stood on the step, patiently waiting for him to appear. One minute, two minutes, three minutes, four and still no show. Now I was just confused. He knew I was coming, so what the hell? I went to the window, and again, no flipping sign. Right. Back to the letterbox, shouting loud and determined. 'Dad! Dad! It's me!'

At which point, a pair of slipper-clad feet came shuffling towards me on the old plastic carpet protector, still stuck in place from the day we'd moved in.

Eventually, and I do mean eventually, he got to the door, with a face like thunder and a mug of strong coffee. 'I'm not ready yet!' He was wearing the 'I've just got out of bed and my head's still banging from the afternoon session, when I got so drunk that I cried, then passed out on the commode' look on his face. Then turning his back, snapped, 'Right, I suppose you'd better come in, then.'

Yes, thought I, now smiling through the rage. *I suppose I had.*

***

I hadn't been to my father's house in a long time. The front room walls were a dark shade of fag-nolia, it was a neglected mess, borderline dilapidated, and had all the signs and symptoms of someone living with a mental illness and in squalor.

I should have gone in there with a flamethrower and some disinfectant. He needed help, but where to start when there was still so much of him I feared? His beard had grown down the length of his chest, and his hair, now totally grey and unkempt, was standing proud on the top of his head.

This was my once so particular, immaculately dressed father, so tall and handsome that he'd turn heads wherever he went. Now, he just looked like he could turn his own. He moved to the dining room and, still silently seething, I followed. The bed social services had installed for Evelynne two years earlier was still in situ and, because of the increasing claudication in his legs, my father, unable to climb the stairs, had made it his own, and quite clearly hadn't changed the sheets for months.

There there was *some* evidence that hand-washing had taken place, from the thermal underpants hanging on the clothes airer, propped firmly against the windowsill, that we passed on our way to the kitchen … but even so.

'I'm making some tea,' he said, stirring a pan of tomato soup with a burnt-out wooden spoon. 'D'you want some?'

It was strange to see him fending for himself and at the cooker. Apart from the bread with the soup, he never really ate solids. I wasn't sure if the loss of appetite was down to his drinking, or just his laziness kicking in.

'No, I'm alright, thanks.' My eyes scanned the tiny off-shot kitchen that hadn't been decorated in twenty years or so. It was sparse: just a filthy old cooker, a scruffy little sink, a bin brimming with crap, and an ancient Hoover twin-tub that hadn't been moved in years, and only existed for the stacking of dirty pots and pans, washed on a need-to-use basis only.

The soup boiled, he dispensed it into a bowl and back to the front room we went.

I waited as he slumped into his tatty brown armchair and placed myself firmly on the sofa, watching the news in silence, until he'd finally devoured the contents of the bowl, throwing it down, spoon and all, onto a coffee table cluttered with the tea-stained envelopes of his unopened post.

Fuck! Someone pass the ectoplasm. This was so fucking depressing, not to mention awkward. I could hear the purr of the taxi still waiting outside. What the hell was he doing? I wanted to scream, slap him out, word for word, with a, 'Get-your-bloody-coat-on!' But in the end, chose: 'D'you want me to do the washing up while you get ready?' instead.

Still nothing. Not a word as he knelt, igniting the fire with a match pulled from a huge yellow box he kept on the mantelpiece. There was a mini explosion of gas as he sat back in his chair. 'You'll have to go without me,' he said, still snappy. *Snap, snap.* 'Ring and let me know how she is.' He lit a fag, this time with a red plastic lighter he'd snatched from his pocket.

'Alright.' I conceded. I knew from past experience that nothing moved him when he was hanging, not even a sick mother. 'I'll call you later.'

And with that, he began to rasp, just like Aqua Lung dying of consumption, as I left by the front door, through a fog of smoke, to the taxi still waiting outside.

***

Arriving at Brearley Ward, I was struck by two things: the stifling heat, and an under-smell of warm mashed potato. I went to the nurses' station and asked where I'd find Evelynne. A chubby nurse with brown hair tied neatly into the nape of her neck was studying some sort of staff rota. 'She's just being seen by doctor. She's at end of the ward, to the left.'

'Thanks, I'll er … I'll wait till he's finished.'

I stood for a while reading the noticeboard and a leaflet on how to spot the first signs of diabetes, until I saw the curtains around Evelynne's bed being pulled back, and what looked like a twelve-year-old doctor walk away at speed towards the nurses' station, with a clipboard and a concerned look on his face.

'Excuse me,' I called as he sped past, 'is it okay if I go and see my grandmother now?'

I pointed towards Evelynne, who was lying on a mountain of pillows, her arm in a sling, like a broken little sparrow on a huge, blue and white marshmallow cloud.

'Sorry,' said the twelve-year-old, 'who are you?'

I know he'd probably been on an eighty-hour shift, without sleep, but surely the words 'grand' and 'mother' were a small hint. 'I'm her granddaughter. Is she alright?'

He brushed a hand through his floppy blonde fringe and, spreading his arms, said, 'Can we talk in the relatives room?'

'Okay.' I followed him down the corridor to a small lounge at the other end of the ward.

'Please,' he said, 'take a seat.'

I could see he was nervous and very, very young. He looked uncomfortable in the way that nice people always do when on the cusp of delivering a shit sandwich.

'The thing is,' he cleared his throat, 'your grandmother is very ill. She had a fall in the early hours at the home and, as a result, has broken her hip and her left wrist, which, in themselves, are not life-threatening injuries. However, due to the more serious fall she had a while ago, her body is finding it hard to fight its way back to full strength, and we have concerns in relation to her blood pressure, which is very low.' He let out a heavy sigh. 'To be honest, we think she may be failing.'

'Failing? I don't understand.'

'What I mean to say is that, at eighty-three years old, she's had a couple of nasty knocks which have taken their toll, and now her body appears to be giving up on her. She just doesn't have the strength to fight off infection and injury in the same way you and I would. She'll need an operation to put her hip right, but currently doesn't have the strength to endure what would be a major procedure. We will, of course, monitor her progress, but for now, pain control is the main priority.' He looked right at me and I still didn't get it. What was he was trying to say? What?

I drew a breath. 'But she'll be alright, won't she?' I could see that this was too direct a question for him to answer. 'She's very resilient. She shakes things off. Really, nothing keeps her down.'

He wasn't buying it. 'Well, she's very poorly and we can't really say, at this stage, whether she'll get back to full strength or not. All we can do is make her as comfortable as possible, and hopefully, we'll know more over the next couple of days.'

He did have a very nice face, fair-skinned, borderline freckle, but right now, I really wanted to punch it … really hard. I'd seen Evelynne at the weekend and she was fine. We had a chat in the television room, I'd bought her some boiled sweets and she was fine, fine, bloody well fine. I needed to see for myself. I knew her better than he did. I'd be the judge of how she'd recover, not him.

'Right, can I see her now. Please?'

'Yes, of course. She's—'

I cut him short. 'At the top of the ward, left-hand side.'

***

On the approach I could see Evelynne was restless, mumbling furiously, her little face wearing an expression of deep concern. I pulled up a chair and sat myself down. 'Hello, sweedie.' I kissed her head. 'Are you alright?'

'Who is it?' She was trying to trace the shape of my face. Her cataracts were worsening and it took time for her to distinguish from person to person. 'Oh, Clare, it's you! Why aren't you at school?'

I thought she probably meant college. 'I don't go to college tonight. That's Wednesday night.'

'But what about your Granddad? He'll want his tea.' She had an intense look. She meant what she said. I'd never seen her like this before, agitated, toiling for the facts, confusing time and space. I finally realised what the doctor was trying to say. She *was* very poorly, and her mind had begun to ramble back, to when Granddad was alive and I was a schoolgirl.

I looked over my shoulder, desperately searching for a nurse who, luckily, was already on the way. 'Hi, I'm Jean, Ward Sister, and I'm looking after your nan.' She was chirpy and nice.

'Hi. I'm Clare, and to be honest, I'm a bit worried.' I looked back at Evelynne, who by now was having a heated conversation with an imaginary other about some stepladders.

'She's just a bit dehydrated having had a nasty knock. But we're feeding fluids through the drip, so hopefully she'll feel a bit better in a few hours' time.' She looked at Evelynne in a genuine, caring sort of way.

'Dehydration? Is that why she's a bit confused?'

'Could be.' She smiled.

Okay, dehydration: I'd take that. She's dehydrated that's all – nothing to worry about here, nothing at all. 'It's just that I have to call my dad and let him know what's happening. He couldn't get here tonight, but he'll definitely be here tomorrow.' Feeling slightly more at ease, until …

'Is your dad the next of kin?'

I dropped the smile.

'We may have to operate on her hip, that's all, and we'll probably need his consent for treatment,' she soothed.

'Oh, yes, right! Yes, yes he is.'

She began straightening Evelynne's bed and the sheets that had become tangled in the fight over the stepladders. 'Alright, Evelynne?' she bellowed, like only ward sisters can.

'I'll av to be, won't I?' Kissing her teeth with a tut. 'But winda's wayn't wesh the sens.'

Jean shot me a puzzled look.

'I think she's referring to the stepladders.' I smiled.

'Oh, okay. But how d'you feel in yourself, then, Evelynne?'

'To be honest, luv, I'm a bit worried.' She was grabbing Jean's tabard.

'What about? There's nowt to worry about here.'

'It's Clare,' she whispered. 'Can you get her a bed? It's bitter outside, an' she's got school int morning.'

'No, Evelynne, don't be silly,' replied Jean, still overloud and deliberate. 'She's got her own bed in her own house. She can't stay here.'

Poor Evelynne, her face was a picture of terror as she turned to meet me full-on. 'Clare, I'm really sorry, but I've got ever such bad news.' She cried.

'What is it? What's the matter?'

'They said you can't stop. I've asked them for a bed, but they said you'll av to gu.'

'No, it's alright. I've got a nice bed of my own. I'll be just fine.' I looked at Jean. 'She over-worries about me. She always has.'

'Ah, she's a lovely old lady. We've all taken quite a shine to her.' She was stroking Evelynne's arm, poking out of her gown like an anaemic twig. 'And she's your dad's mum?'

'Yes, and you're right to love her. She's very special.'

'All nans are special tho, aren't they?'

Right. No disrespect to Jean, but she didn't have a clue, Evelynne wasn't just a 'nan'. I wanted to explain, like I always wanted to explain to everyone I'd ever met. I should have said 'mother' because that's what she was. To call her 'nan' was completely demoting her importance. Should I explain? No, not really, there'd be no point.

'Right,' said Jean, now checking her upside-down watch. 'I'll leave you to it. I'm just at the nurses' station if you need anything else.' And with that, she was gone.

I pulled in closer, but Evelynne was drifting into a doze, knackered out, no doubt, by the fight over the stepladder. So I reached to take her hand, her tiny little hand, still wearing the silver snake that Granddad William had won for her on the last night of the fair, the very first night they'd met. It had emerald-green eyes and a ruby-red tongue, its limbless, marcasite body always wrapped so tightly round her pretty little finger. But her refusal to take it off had caused all the stones to become dislodged as she'd scrubbed dishes, washed clothes, cooked, cleaned, ironed and shopped, fed the dog, deflead the cat, changed the beds and emptied the potties, not forgetting to put the milk checks out, while speed-balling a thousand pairs of socks – all at the same time.

She'd worn her poor little body out being our mother: sitting patiently at the school play, as we sang and tapped our way through obscure versions of old Christmas classics; nursing us when we were sick; worrying when we went out, and staying out of her bed until we finally returned. She was feeding beaks, saving our lives, going without so we could go with, and now she was fading, I knew it, and despite the confusion, so did she. She looked at me now, as I silently sat, until slowly and safely she fell to her sleep.

***

Over the next few days, her condition worsened and she became weaker and weaker. She asked me and Frances to take her hands, before falling back into unconsciousness once more. So, after another long night, we kissed our goodbyes, with a promise to meet the very next day.

In the early hours of the morning my father called and told me I should make my way to the hospital immediately. I got dressed, called a cab and raced off to meet him, finally hitting Brearley Ward with a full-on sprint, when up popped Jean, grabbing my arm and slowing me to a stop.

'Clare! Clare! I'm really sorry, but your nan died about twenty minutes ago.' I looked at her with some confusion. What a thing to say! 'Your dad was with her. In fact, he's there now. Just go steady. Are you alright?' Now she really was asking for a kick in the face, as I pushed her off and continued on my way, to the broken little sparrow and the curtains now tightly drawn around her bed.

No longer propped up by a thousand white pillows, she was tucked in tight and laid out flat – flat and motionless. My father was sitting on a chair, holding her hand. I moved to his side, not daring to take my eyes from Evelynne, as he fell into my arms and started to weep. How could this be? I'd made her a promise, a promise to come back, to say night night, and now she was gone? Before I'd even arrived?

I placed my father back into his chair and, rising to my feet, swept a tiny lock of light brown hair from her perfect little forehead. Her milky skin, still clear and bright, was soft and warm: not cold and dead, but soft and warm as I kissed her face and closed her eyes, her beautiful eyes, always and forever the gentlest of blue, all gracious, all doting and flecked with love. Then, stifling a compulsion to scream the place down, I silently started to shake.

'Is Frances with you?' My father was mumbling.

'No,' I whispered, 'but the traffic's bad. She'll be here soon.'

'Right,' he snapped, wiping the tears from his eyes. 'I'm going outside, I don't want her walking in here without knowing what's happened.'

And as he left, I felt a relief, not just from the burden of his pain and sorrow, but a relief to be alone with Evelynne once more, like when I was little and she painted me pictures with the snapshots of her life: the long hot summers, when cockroaches infested the bed she shared with her siblings; how her mother would take them outside, to sleep on the cold stone steps, until the council came round to spray water on the tiny back-to-back houses, in an attempt to cool and curb the infestation. Evelynne had loved her mother, who'd borne twelve children, four of whom had died in infancy due to extreme poverty, and another, Evelynne's brother, lost at just eighteen years old, like so many others, to the carnage of war.

Evelynne was the youngest child and her life had been hard. Hard from beginning to end. A daughter, a sister, a wife, a mother, she was always someone's something, never just herself – never just Evelynne.

I sat twisting the snake around her tiny finger, wishing I could rewrite her life, put her in another time, another place: a place where her intelligence wasn't thwarted by the mundanity of housework and childcare; a place free from the slavery; a place where she sipped afternoon tea, elegantly dressed in her best green dress, away from the poverty and hardship that had come to define her life. I looked around at this, her last place: a depressing place, an unworthy place. She really did deserve so much more.

Evelynne was a beacon, a force of light, a light never dimmed by the constant toil and worry of us. She'd taken us in, grown us up and danced us through the storm, from the Gay Gordons to the Last Waltz. Dancing, dancing and singing – that was us. And now, through the choke of inconsolable tears, I could hear her voice, and she was singing still.

I sat twisting the snake, until I heard the clatter of my sister's shoes getting louder and louder as she approached the curtain still drawn around us.

***

'Basically, there are three types of urn, depending on how much you want to spend,' said Ian, as we sat in his office at the funeral directors. 'The most expensive and, in my opinion, the most tasteful, is the Hardwick: a mahogany case with a brass-effect name plate.' He pointed to the base. 'And for this price, we include the engraving. Next is the Talbot: a less expensive alternative in ash, with stainless-steel fixtures and fittings, so to speak. This is also a very nice option if cost is at issue. And finally, the most inexpensive is the Cavendish: a screw-top urn-type container, made from plastic, no fittings, and usually used for a scattering rather than interment.' He pushed the samples across the desk, Hardwick first, and we examined them one by one.

'I don't think so,' said Frances, picking up the plastic talcum powder bottle that was the Cavendish, disgust written all over her face.

'This looks like it should contain lily of the valley, not the dearly departed!' She pushed it back towards him. 'And furthermore, cost is not the issue here!' She was offended, but without need. Ian was a very nice man, trying to do a very difficult job, in very difficult circumstances. I was almost certain that the Cavendish had mortified him just as much, and he had to push the bloody thing to sale. She really should have cut him some slack.

I cut in. 'I think we're agreed, it's got to be the first one. So if you could add that to the list and maybe let us have a price, we'll get out of your hair.' Which was a really stupid thing to have said, because Ian didn't have any hair. My defusing was always riddled with insult, no matter how well meant.

In an attempt to keep busy and limit my father's distress, Frances and I had decided that we would arrange Evelynne's funeral. We'd chosen the best coffin the insurance policy could afford, and the urn was the last item on the list before we went to the florist to order flowers.

But the funeral was hideous.

I just wanted to get away from the madness of my delinquent dad who, out of control and quite clearly off his tits, had asked the funeral director if he wouldn't mind dropping him off at the nearest newsagent for a packet of fags, and then perhaps the pub?

Incredulous at the request, the chauffeur actually agreed, so up the Wicker they went, empty hearse an' all, to GT News and the Corner Pin.

***

It was on a crisp and cold October day that we finally laid Evelynne to rest, but the sun was out and streaming through the mature trees in the old cemetery. The vicar stood at the foot of the grave waiting for us to arrive, Bible in hand. His kind smile welcomed us as we took our places to recite the Lord's Prayer. The stone, which was small and sunk, bore the initials of Granddad William, and Evelynne's mother and father, and of course, 'EH' once interment had taken place.

Still clinging to the Hardwick, Frances bent to reunite Evelynne with Granddad William, who, to our shock and surprise, was currently residing in the talcum powder bottle. I looked at Frances, and she at me, and in that moment, we realised just how stupid Evelynne would have regarded our sentimental overspend. Always good with her money, she'd been frugal to the end. We, on the other hand, had completely failed to grasp the point. Once you're dead, you're dead; it matters not a jot whether you reside in mahogany or plastic. It's the relationships with others that live on after death: the things we do and the love we share, not the wood and hardware, not the Hardwick, Talbot or Cavendish.

I winked at Frances and we broke a smile, as the vicar kindly blessed her soul.

***

On the way back, Frances and I took a detour to the rest home, so that we could sort out Evelynne's things, do the charity-shop run, select our keepsakes and finalise things with the home sister, who'd been so very upset by her passing.

As we entered the little pink room, all was still, in a silence broken only by the songs of the birds in the garden outside. Her curtains were open revealing the tiny pink plant, still in bloom. Her bed was made, but her chair was empty. It was then, and only then, that the unmistakable gulf left by her absence became all too real.

I moved to the bed. A tiny brushed-cotton nightdress was folded neatly on her pillow, as though waiting for her return. Inside was a label with her name on, one of the many Frances had sewn into her clothing when she'd first gone into the home just two years before. I pulled it to my chest and sat in her chair, trying to get her essence from its teeny little collar, and started to cry.

'Come on,' said Frances, clearing her throat. 'She's not poorly any more. We've got to be grateful for that.'

'I know, but I think it's all our fault. I think we made her tired.'

She knelt down. 'No. No, we didn't, and you shouldn't think like that. She wouldn't have had it any other way. She loved us; we were her children.' Then, pulling out a tissue, she quickly dabbed her eyes. 'You know, when someone's poorly,' she said, 'you want them to live, but I was thinking the other night, why? Why did we want her to live when she

128

was so ill? For ourselves, not for her, because if we'd wanted the best for her, it was to let her go.'

I knew my sister was right. Evelynne had been so very poorly, but the pain of not seeing her again had totally overwhelmed me and I was really struggling with the loss.

'Right,' said Frances, rising to her feet. 'Let's make a start. If we do it together, it won't be so bad. Come on, you take the wardrobe and I'll take the—' She stopped short, her eyes firmly fixed on the tiny table chair-side. I followed her gaze, and there, on the white lace doily, next to the cassette player, sat two little sweets. Evelynne must have got them from the glass jar the night before her fall, ready for her mid-morning book; an unfinished book she never came back to. I pictured her choosing the colours, one pink, one green, placing them carefully on the table, before climbing into bed.

And in that moment, my heart finally gave in and broke, not with a shatter or a crack, but a thud, a flattening, life-changing, irrecoverable thud. Those two little sweets, the ten-ton wrecking ball of that final, lethal, smash in the face.

I wasn't born from love, but through Evelynne I'd come to know it and nothing in my life mattered more to me than she. I buried my head back into her nightdress and, as the salty tears continued to flow, I knew this love, this one true love, would never pass, would never die.

Coincidence Technology

Bereavement is weird and grief takes on many guises, particularly when it involves the death of a parent. We learn the hard way that there's no longer anything between us and it, that life is transient and mortality short.

In the immediate aftermath of Evelynne's death, the feeling of having nothing left to lose had empowered me. It was time to stop banging my head against the brick wall of ambition and smash my way through it instead. So for the next two years, I continued to climb the post-privatisation corporate ladder, adhering to the more traditional route of qualifications, hard work and a determination to succeed, rather than a determination to suck ass, as per the modus operandi of the Muttley crew.

In 1995 the Claims Department was bought out by an insurance company with a very different ethos from that of old British Coal, and I, in turn, had taken on more and more claims accounts, with one in particular – a miners' union.

The Union of Democratic Mineworkers, aka the UDM, had a small number of low-value claims they wanted to bring against UK Coal, the private company that now owned the majority of operational deep mines. However, owing to a change in the law, which ruled that if a claim was worth less than £1,000, although the claimant was still legally entitled to receive compensation, costs would not be paid to solicitors for handling them. The reason being, that solicitors' costs were, more often than not, proving to be greater than the total value of the claim itself, and so it was deemed unreasonable for an employer to have to pay more in solicitors' costs than they were paying by way of compensation to the claimant, for what appeared to be very small, very straightforward claims.

This had left the union with a dilemma: they still wanted to pursue claims for their members regardless of value, but their representing solicitors did not want to take on claims they would not be paid for. The solution was to allow the UDM to bring these small-value claims, albeit without costs, and enter into an agreement whereby disbursements, for things like photographs and medical reports, would be reimbursed.

True to form, Derek, his handlebar moustache and his gaggle of repressed bailiffs, did not want to dirty their claims' profile with the insignificant injuries of a 'tin pot' union, particularly one as controversial as this.

'Scabs and their fucking cut bums? No thanks!' snapped the angry hamster, taking some sort of political high ground, which was odd, if not a little bit hypocritical, given that Derek had also worked through the miners' strike, squeezing past the pickets on his way to the staff canteen for a coffee, three sugars and a double bacon bun.

'Well,' I said, 'I quite enjoy a precipice. I'll do it. I'll take the cut bums.'

***

The first time I met Mick Stevens, General Secretary of the UDM, was when he arrived at the office to discuss his low-value claims. Discussions were common practice and usually conducted between plaintiff and defendant in an attempt to settle cases without the need to go to court. I'd booked a small conference room for me, Mick and Mick's assistant, Jackie, along with the usual comestibles from the staff canteen for the post-discussion buffet. Although I'd spoken to Mick on the phone, we'd never actually met, and in my imagination he'd been a cloth-cap colonel, a fusion of Arthur Scargill and the one-eyed barman from the Wheel Tappers and Shunters, so when he finally hit reception, I was pleasantly surprised to find that he was neither.

He was very tall with rosy cheeks and a dark receding hairline. He wore a tweed jacket, shirt with tie, and smart beige trousers – more farmer than packer.

'Hey up! You must be Clare,' his broad Nottinghamshire accent was round and friendly.

'Yes,' I said, shaking a huge purple hand, which was cold to the touch, the only mining giveaway. 'Nice to meet you.'

'This is Jackie.' He thumb-pointed to a small-framed woman in a red polo-necked jumper to his left. 'She helps mi now an' agen wi stuff int office, an' she's bin sortin out claims we've sent.'

Leaning in, Jackie held out a very small, very warm hand. 'Hello,' she said, 'nice to meet you.'

'And you. Shall we go up to the conference room and make a start?'

'Good idea,' said Mick, as we set off for the lift.

**

The discussion had gone well.

According to Mick, we were 'Only a gnat's knacker apart in valuation', and 'Not choppin bloody trees dine either, wi chuffin tit-for-tat letters, flying back an' bloody forth'. Which, of course, was, 'Complete bleedin bollocks, when at end ont day, we can sit dine like proper adults and thrash things out'.

I agreed, and come to think of it, I really liked this Mick Stevens and his no-angle, no-slant, no-messing approach. He was refreshingly authentic and open to the point of transparent – in stark contrast to the impenetrable facade of an emotionally constipated hard-boiled lawyer, happy to skin a flea in order to score a point.

'Thing is, Clare,' he said, much later with his eyebrows in knots, 'nobdy gus tu work tu get hurt, an' it dunt do union any good if stragglers aren't looked after. To be honest, mate, it's not *our* costs I'm worried about, but I am bit worried about sendin any more on our claims tut lawyers. We're gerrin monthly bills, an' it's costing union a bloody fortune.'

Historically, unions always had a preferred firm of solicitors that specialised in union work. I didn't quite understand why it should be costing the union anything. In fact, they should be benefiting from giving this firm so much work, not paying for the privilege.

I told him to open up negotiations with his lawyers, and if they refused to budge, instruct another firm to act for the union. He said he'd give it some serious thought: 'Summert's got tu give.' Grabbing a small tuna triangle in a huge purple fist. 'Union'll be bloody bankrupt if wi carry on way wi are.'

It was official, I definitely liked this Mick Stevens. He was benevolent by nature and genuine in his concern. So, labels aside, I was happy to have discussed with scab, as we finished our lunch and I took them back down to reception.

'Ever thought on workin fot other side then, Clare?' he asked as we said goodbye.

'Not really. I'm up for a big interview next week, so I hope I'll get promoted.'

'Well, if it dunt come off, gi me a ring. Union could use a worker bee like you.' And with that, he was gone, with his full and final offers tucked safely under his arm.

***

I'd prepared very well for my interview, which was to consist of two parts: a death-by-PowerPoint presentation, followed by a full-on, sit-down grilling by a panel of senior management.

Although this was post privatisation, most of the FOMTs had been kept in place for the handover, and the position I was being interviewed for was to drive the department through the privatisation process. The Claims Department was on the cusp of two major pieces of litigation being brought by a group of solicitors representing miners for injuries sustained as a result of using handheld percussive tools within their occupation. This industrial disease, more commonly known as Vibration White Finger (VWF), was currently being pursued through the courts via a handful of test cases, and a judgment was pending. Should these test cases be successful and British Coal found liable, then thousands of other miners would also be eligible to make a claim.

Additionally, in another separate piece of litigation, more test cases were being heard to decide whether or not British Coal was liable for causing breathing difficulties in miners as a direct result of their working conditions. This class action was known generically as 'The British Coal Respiratory Disease Litigation', and again, should the lead cases prove successful, then thousands of miners would be eligible to make claims for Chronic Obstructive Pulmonary Disease (COPD), which, like the cases for VWF, would need to be defended.

We would handle the claims on behalf of the government, who now had liability to pay compensation because British Coal as a nationalised industry no longer existed.

I'd worked day and night on my presentation and had gone into minute detail on how to handle thousands of potential claims by implementing the principles of the pilot Sarah and I had set up, the blueprint of which had been very successful in defending cases on behalf of UK Coal.

But Sarah was long gone, having passed the mantle of nutcracker onto me, and now it was up to me to keep her legacy going and not give in to the negative enforcement brigade.

In retrospect, I suppose it was slightly naive to expect the Ye Olde Men of Yore to grasp the concept of progress. They were still coming to terms with the fact that Queen Victoria was dead, and had no idea what I meant by the 'We need to ensure IT supports business activity, not the other way round' speech, or 'How a diary-led claims system is the only way to bulk-handle claims efficiently'.

They sat in blind indifference until I'd completed my presentation, then bombarded me with questions like: Did I really see the office becoming paper-free? How was it possible to make a profit and spend thousands on a new IT system? Why wasn't the current IT system adequate? What did it all mean? Had I banged my head on a mangle?

Honestly, I thought they'd get it. They didn't ... and gave the job to Gerald. Gerald, who, if he'd been a word, then that word would have been Dull. Dull, undynamic, sweat-marked, blind as a bat, but too vain to wear glasses, friend of the panel Gerald. Gerald, who'd told the rest of us not to bother applying because the job was his anyway. Gerald, who called men by their first name, and women 'luv'. Gerald, who wore shiny grey trousers that had started life black, but had been in the boil-wash way too many times, then ironed on the wrong side; shiny grey trousers he'd teamed with glossy purple shirts sometime in the early 1970s, a look he hadn't thought to update since. That Gerald.

In the post-interview feedback, I sat in silence, trying to avoid his gingivitis, as he told me that my presentation hadn't really been understood by the panel, and I might as well have been speaking Swahili.

The post-interview feedback culminating in, 'Come on, you can't possibly have thought you were up to it. I mean, you didn't really think

134

they'd give a job like this to someone like you, did you?'

I looked at him with some pity as he leant back in his chair, sweat stains akimbo, wondering how anyone could be so smug and superior, yet so unenlightened, and all at the same time.

Poor Gerald. He didn't have an inkling of the shitstorm about to engulf his Department of Claim. So, in an effort to refrain from spitting pure venom all over his best lap-dancing shirt, I responded with what can only be described as controlled resentment, when I told him to shove his job and his office away-days up his fat, shiny arse, along with the bottle of deodorant that still appeared to be stuck in his in-tray. And with that, marched out, leaving a gobsmacked Gerald to sit and ponder over a crap cup of coffee, a soft custard cream and a blank feedback form.

***

Two days of seething had told me that it was now time to run at speed from the cliché.

I'd worked my bony arse off juggling two jobs, passed my exams with distinction, won the bloody Student of the Year award, taken on the pilot team and made it work, cleared the backlog of colliery investigations without assistance, or encouragement, and still they thought me incapable. It wasn't the long hours that finally burnt me out, it was the constant undermining. No, there really was no two ways about it: what with the above facts and Shiny Arse Gate, I had to leave.

Sarah had told me many times that true high-flyers walked if they didn't get what they wanted. I thought about Mick and the offer he'd made, and decided I'd look into walking.

***

Arriving at the union offices on Berry Hill Lane, I was already besotted.

This old NUM-turned-UDM-after-the-miners'-strike building sat peacefully with itself on perfectly manicured lawns, the back of which faced out onto open playing fields.

Entering reception was a bit like stepping back in time, with a decor that must have seemed quite cutting-edge in the 1950s: clean lines, plywood panels and abstract lampshades – it was a full-weight Planet

Retro.

I approached a small serving hatch and behind it sat Jackie, who appeared to be doubling as the receptionist. 'Hello, Clare,' she chirped, reaching for the handset of a cord circuit switch. 'I'll just let Mr Stevens know you're here.' And, after announcing my arrival, quickly marched me down a long narrow corridor to a room labelled 'The Executive Suite'.

'Would you like a coffee? The tea lady's doing her trolley round and I can get you one if you like.'

'Yes, please. A coffee would be great.' They had a tea lady? With a trolley? This had to be 1957, I was sure of it, as just moments later she returned with a small china cup, brimming to its top with coffee made from milk, like a bedtime Ovaltine.

'I've brought you some sugar. I didn't know if you—' She stopped mid-sentence, so I nervously cut in.

'No, no, I don't, thanks.'

'Right.' She smiled, making an exit. 'Mr Stevens won't be long.'

I stood in front of the double-glazed doors, gazing out over the vast expanse of lawn. A small grey squirrel with an acorn in its mouth was running up an ancient oak, disappearing round the trunk, to the back and out of sight. It really was very nice.

'Barbara! Get Beryl to fetch me a coffee fromt trolley an' tell her tu bring it down tut EC room!' I heard Mick's voice bellowing down the corridor, and a breathy, high-pitched female in reply:

'Yes, Mr Stevens.'

That made me chuckle as the door to the Executive Suite swung open and in marched Mick, with A.N. Other following closely behind.

'Alreight, duck, finally got here, then?' he said, stretching out for a handshake.

'Yes.' I smiled. 'Sorry, I'm late. I had trouble finding it. Glad I did, though. It's a lovely spot. I've just been watching a squirrel.'

'Ah, yeah, that's Cyril, UDM squirrel, an' this is Neil, UDM President.' He thumb-pointed to a small man with greying hair and an equally greying beard framing a ruddy lived-in face.

'Alreight,' he said. 'Mick's told mi a lot about you.' He held out a hand covered in home-made tattoos, nicotine-stained fingers giving his forty-a-day habit away.

'Nice to meet you.' I shook his hand and we took our seats.

'Where's bleedin Beryl wi that drink?' Mick was getting louder, eager to show he was boss. I could hear the rattle of a tea trolley pulling up outside the door, and in walked the tea lady, overall and all, with drinks for Mick and Neil, and a pile of assorted biscuits on a small, patterned plate.

'Ta, luv,' said Mick, snatching a digestive, then, pleasantries aside, went straight to business. 'Nythen, I've spoke to Neil about what we intend doing wi these claims, but you were saying summert about lawyers costs?'

'Yes. I know that you have just one firm that the union always uses.' I took a sip of coffee; it really was very good.

'Eye, that's right. Used 'em for years, Clare.' His eyes now firmly fixed on me, he was hanging on my every word.

'And you refer all claims to them except, of course – as a result of a recent change in the law – those that are valued at less than £1,000?'

'Reight agen.' He moved forward in his seat.

'So you refer all cases without anyone at the union reviewing whether or not the claim has any prospect of success, then the solicitors take on the claim and start running up costs and disbursements?' I asked, but I knew the answer to the question.

'What's disbursements?' Now Neil was showing interest. The scar on the end of his nose was prominent at this angle. It looked like someone or something had bitten it off, and that at some stage it'd been inadvertently stitched back on, by a cack-handed medical centre attendant, eager to get off shift.

I paused for a moment's thought. It's true what they say: comrades don't do sexy. 'Disbursements are things like medical reports, mining reports, photographs, that sort of thing. Y'know … the evidence that supports the claim.' Trying really hard not to stare the snout down.

'Ah, reight.' He got out a fag and started to light up.

So I continued. 'The problem is, once the claim is live and running the union is immediately at risk for costs, and if the case goes to

137

court, then court costs too.'

'Eye, we've had all this wit canteen workers.' Mick nodded his agreement.

'My point is,' I said, determined to finish, 'win, lose or draw the lawyers are getting paid and the union is picking up the bill.'

'But int that how it should be, then, Clare? We do get most ont money we've laid out when they get paid, but that can tek as long as three, maybe five years, more in a big case, an' it's that cash flow that's bolloxing us up.'

'No, Mick, seriously, that type of financial support needs to stop. There should be an agreement in place whereby the union can assess the validity of each claim – does it have any chance of success? If not, the claimant needs to be told that the union is unable to pursue the claim and reasons for that need to be given, along with any notice surrounding the limitation period. In cases that are worthy of pursuing, the lawyers should be able to operate a much more collaborative case management system, updating the union on the progress of each and every claim from intimation right through to final settlement. This not only allows the union to monitor and manage the process in a more cost-effective way, but has the added bonus of streamlining the system for the benefit of its members. If, on the other hand, a case needs to go to court to be resolved, then the union needs to sit down with the lawyer, review the facts of the case and the prospects of success. The union could still support the case financially or, as an option, effect some after-the-event insurance, whereby the union funds the policy to cover any adverse costs. This gives the union an element of control in relation to the case management of legal fees and disbursements, rather than blindly taking the financial hit time and time again, for cases that should never have got to court in the first place.' I hardly drew breath.

'Ha! Told you she were brilliant, dint I?' Mick was turning to Neil.

'So,' said Neil, exhaling fag smoke from his bottom lip up, 'would that be part on your job, if you come tu wok for us, then?'

'Yes. I'd make it my first job to review the policy you currently have with your lawyers and maybe set up a preferred list of firms for you to consider. This would not only give the union more choice, but more choice to the miners, and add an element of competition into the mix, for what has always been a secure income stream for just one firm. We also need to make sure that we pass on good cases and wheedle out rogue claims. The system also needs to be fair to the lawyers, and fair to the miners who have genuine claims. We want to be taken seriously by the other side. We don't want a reputation for making spurious claims. I also think claimants prefer to be told from the outset whether they have a valid claim or not. They don't want leading down a path of expectation only to have the door slammed firmly in their face a few months later – it's not a good practice for the union to adopt.'

'Great!' snapped Mick, and direct as ever: 'D'you want job then?'

Did I want the job?

Yes, I think I did, but not on the I-work-my-arse off, you-collect-the-fee terms, I had in my current position. I'd had enough of the exploitative, slave labour, claims management shit. I needed to be incentivised financially, and wasn't going to settle for anything less.

'I do,' and looking straight at them, 'but how much are you willing to pay?'

'Truth is, Clare,' Mick's tone much more serious now, 'because ont lawyers' bills an' pit closures an' the like, we can't offer you much now, but what we can say is that if it is successful we'll agree to pay an incentive bonus, based on how many claims you turn over an' how much money you bring in tut union. A bit like way miners are paid at pit level.'

'So how much were you thinking?'

'We think twelve grand a year, but if it dunt look like its working after't first six months, you gu your way, an' we'll gu ours, wi no bad feeling or strings attached.'

I thought about it. That was a lot less than I was on now, and there was the travel from Sheffield to Mansfield. I was still up to my neck in County Court Judgments, still working two jobs just to pay off the debt and survive. If I couldn't make it work, I'd be out on my arse.

Then again, and on the upside, this was an opportunity and a chance to start with a completely blank page, to work and make something better, something successful, something that was mine, my very own Department of Claim. I thought about Sarah, and her steely determination. I knew what she'd do.

'Well,' thinking out loud, 'that's a lot less than I'm on now, an' it's all such a gamble. If it doesn't work, then I'm out of a job. I mean, it's not like we've got any claims to handle yet, an' who's to say that the defendants will even want to deal with us direct? We're not solicitors and then there's all that strike shit. We'd be fighting uphill.'

'Well, exactly, mate. You're gonna hav tu earn your corn, that's why we agree tu pay you a bonus.' Mick was showing signs of concern that I might walk away, and given the dwindling numbers in membership, his union would run out of funds.

I stood up. 'Alright, pay me £12,000 basic, plus a bonus of, say, three per cent of any income I generate for the union, and we've got a deal.'

They sat in silence. Mick reached for another biscuit. 'So,' he said, 'you get three per cent, an union gets other ninety-seven?'

'Yes …' (I know, I know, looking back now, I could even smack myself).

'Alreight,' said Neil, rising to his feet. 'It's a deal. An' when wi shek hands here, we don't gu back on us word.'

I looked at his chewed nose, and took his hand. 'Agreed.'

'Right,' said Mick. 'When can you start?'

Broken Ties Trump Broken Hearts

That weekend I went home and devised my letter of resignation. I'd meant to hand it in on Monday, but decided on Tuesday instead, in order to give Gerald, the world's first talking daffodil, time to brace himself.

Mondays were always busy. In addition to a caseload of claims, I had two ball-breakers at the gym after work. So it wasn't until 10.00 p.m., with my hair stuck to my face, swallowing watery sick, that I finally arrived home, to yet another screeching phone.

I threw down my bag, leapt into the kitchen and, headbutting the corner cabinet, grabbed at the receiver. 'Hello!'

No one there.

'Hello?'

'Is that Clare?'

'Yes, it's Clare.'

'Sorry … it's just that didn't sound like you—'

'Right?'

'—anyway, hello Clare, it's Elizabeth.'

Elizabeth? Blimey, I hadn't spoken to her in a long time. Not since the one thing holding us all together Evelynne – had died, leaving fertile ground for a good old-fashioned family fallout.

We'd each grieved in different ways, but communication (or the lack thereof) had left my sister and I clinging on to old resentments, with neither side prepared nor willing to even attempt to make things right.

And although I hadn't exactly put her in a box (a box labelled: 'ESTRANGED'), she was in 'File Pending', awaiting categorisation as I continued to mull the potential pitfalls of a complete and utter dislocation.

No, I hadn't spoken to Elizabeth in a long time – we were most definitely on the out … So, was this the 'tin-lid' moment? – I braced myself.

'Oh, erm … hello Elizabeth, long time no speak.'

'Indeed, and sorry to bother you now, of course.' Her voice, like her, was flat and cold.

'No, no it's no bother, how can I help?' (Back in claims mode: seriously, what the fuck was wrong with me?)

'I don't want any *help*,' she snarled. 'I just thought I'd let you know that my dad died on Friday.'

I took a step back.

I'm sure she just said that *her* dad had died.

What did she mean?

Who died on Friday?

'Sorry, Elizabeth, who died on Friday?'

'My dad ...'

I moved to the sofa and sat myself down.

I hadn't seen much of my father either, not since he'd been so nasty at the funeral: the wreath I'd bought wasn't big enough; the tears I cried weren't wet enough. He had to pick a fight with someone, and that someone, on that day, had been me.

In times of emotional turmoil, he'd often indulge in rude and abusive behaviour like that: over-focusing on the flaws of others and chewing them out in a narcissistic rage. He exhausted everyone around him, and I was drained by the one-way traffic, having always given him the benefit of the doubt, and received nothing in return. Except, of course, a thin skin, crippling insecurity and small-airways disease from all the passive smoking.

'Clare!' My sister was barking. 'Are you still there?' And in a very brittle tone, which, to be honest, I was beginning to find quite rude.

'Of course I'm still here, but I don't understand. How did it—?'

'We're not quite sure. We'll find out more after the post-mortem.'

'Right.' And I wasn't 'quite sure' who the 'we' were either.

'Although, the cause,' she said, 'isn't really the issue, is it?'

'Is it not?'

'No. The fact is, he died at home and all on his own – poor old soul.'

So, my father dies on Friday, and Elizabeth arrives at his house for the weekend and clears it out, before returning home to break the news with all the charm and compassion of a rattlesnake. Now she really could kiss the left side of my Irish arse. Had she forgotten how he hadn't spoken to her for years after she'd committed the mortal sin of falling in love with some he hadn't approved of? I wanted to scream right back, but chose instead to keep myself calm and, just like her, cold to the touch.

'Well, I hope you haven't put your back out getting on that high horse of yours, Elizabeth. He died Friday, you say, but you chose Monday to call?'

'As usual, I don't know what you're banging on about, or what difference it makes to your little life? I mean, it's not like you cared or anything like that, is it?'

'Okay, we both know that factually, that's insane, but go on, if it makes you feel better, sick it up.'

'Look,' she snapped, 'I didn't particularly want to make this call. In fact, if I'm being honest, I never really wanted to speak to you agen.'

'And yet, here we are.'

'Yes, because that's what decent people do, Clare. It's called doing the right thing.'

'Honest and decent? You? Really?' Now shaking with anger. 'Have you called Frances?'

'Of course I've called Frances.'

'Right, fuck off then!'

So, now it was official. The disaffection was complete.

Our linchpin was gone.

The dynamics had changed.

And into the box she went.

***

Frances was devastated. She'd been excommunicated too but, unlike me, had held out the hope of a reconciliation at some point in time. Unfortunately, my father – a man who never gave in – was stubborn to the end, and the time for a reconciliation had passed, leaving Frances to wrestle with her unresolved issues and the ensuing guilt of an undeserved remorse.

Pouring red wine into what looked more like a vat than a glass, she turned to me in tears. 'You see, I can't understand why he couldn't

143

just have loved us.' She was gulping down hard and fast between sobs. 'We were such cute little kids. It's not like we were naughty. Y'know, sometimes when I look at the photographs of us when we were little, it really makes me want to cry. We're smiling for the camera but we're not happy. You can see it in our eyes. We're not happy.'

'I don't think any of that matters now, Frances. We were just children, he was the grown-up, not us. Besides, you can't negotiate with a lunatic. It wouldn't have mattered what we did, good or bad, he was always going to find fault. Just thank God we had Evelynne. Because one way or another, I really do think he would've killed us.'

'I know,' she said. 'Constantly protecting and defusing, what a nightmare that must have been.' She cleared her throat. 'Y'know, I once asked her why she did it … y'know … took us on. After all, we weren't her kids and she'd just settled down to retirement with Granddad William. And d'you know what she said?'

'Go on.' I knew there was no stopping her.

'She said, "You were just three little girls who didn't have a mum." See, that was her all over: putting everyone else first.'

'But she *was* our mother, Frances, and what's more, she knew what he was like. She'd never have left us alone with him.' I took my sister's hand, determined to highlight the point, but there was a disconnect as she pushed her glass forward for a refill.

'But if he'd only told us the truth, he could have been himself, we wouldn't have judged.' She sat back, leaning on the kitchen wall, her full glass clutched firmly to her chest.

'What d'you mean? Told us what?' I was filling my own.

'Y'know, if he'd told us upfront, we'd have still loved him.'

'Loved him? I think we did love him when we were little, but he pushed us away, then battered it out of us, just to make sure. Like a little tin god on a big wooden stool, playing one child off against the other, deciding which one of us he liked today. That's not a father Frances, that's just fucking cruel.'

'I know, I know, I know. I get that he was controlling, and I *know* he was cruel, but honestly? I think he was terrified of us finding out.'

'Again, I have absolutely no idea what you're talking about. Find out about what? That he was a serial killer? ... What?'

She was staring right at me, like some accuser, like I was the one holding back, but I wasn't – I didn't know my father at all, never mind any of his secrets. 'For fuck's sake, Frances, just say it!'

Silence.

'*Say it!*'

'That he was gay! Dad, he ... he was gay.'

I stared, open-mouthed. 'I'm sorry, what? ... Gay? As in G-A-Y, gay?'

'Don't tell me you didn't know!'

'I didn't ... really, I didn't. I mean, I don't.' I sank some wine. 'Gay? And you know this because ...?'

She put the glass down. 'Right,' she said, sitting up straight. 'Remember when I left home, and he cut me off?'

'Of course I do. He was vile.'

'He didn't speak to me for years, Clare; for years, and I was only sixteen.'

'I know, Frances, but he did it to us all. We all had our *Fiddler on the Roof* moment. It wasn't just you.'

'You're not listening! I hated him and that's why I traced the Birth Mother, to get her side: why she left. I knew there'd be a reason. It can't have just been our fault.' The tears were flowing thick and fast, rolling down her cheeks, and forming a tiny well at the base of her throat.

'Right. It wasn't our fault. But go on, what did she say?'

'She said she'd have to get in bed with us sometimes, because he'd bring his boyfriends home.'

'Really? And you think she was telling the truth?'

'Well, why make *that* up?'

'I don't know. It's a bit obscure, I'll give you that. But then agen, she never stayed in touch, did she? Even when you'd tried so hard to find her, so in a way, she had nothing to lose by dropping you a gay bomb and sticking the blame on him.'

'Suppose not, but it's not just that. Why d'you think he never had a girlfriend? Like, ever? And what about Uncle Tom? Who d'you think he was, then?'

I sat back in my chair, as the cogs in my brain began to turn along with the regurgitation of memories and conversations past, in an attempt to grasp the nettle, the prickle of my father's truth.

Apart from the obvious – his dress sense, a love of opera, Dirk Bogarde and James Dean – central to everything were 'The Uncle Tom Years'. As a child, I'd sneak to the window and see them stepping out into the night, laughing like two college boys, so tall, so handsome and so glad to be alive. Uncle Tom, a constant companion for such a long time, and then never seen again, in the way you don't see your lovers again, when they finally become ex.

Then there were the things he'd say when the gin went in and the truth came out. 'You see, doll face, I always wanted kids, but I never a wanted a wife, know what I mean?'

I told him I did, but I didn't.

I'd always viewed my father as being asexual, like some sort of root vegetable, reproducing via a method of binary fission. I never humanised him in any way, and now, sitting here in my sister's kitchen, it suddenly all made sense, and the last thirty-four years of my life snapped slap bang into place.

All the times he'd tried to keep us from making contact with the Birth Mother, I thought it was because he'd been frightened of losing us, that she'd take us away. I thought the tears were that of a jilted husband, unable to come to terms with the loss of his wife.

I was wrong, wrong, wrong. His pain was that of fear: fear that we'd discover his truth, and for what? It mattered not a jot whether he was gay or straight, who he chose to love, as long as he was happy. But he wasn't happy, he was sad most of the time and now, it was all too late. The acceleration of his alcoholism when Granddad William died must have been the result of a deep-seated regret, of someone who'd put his life on hold in order to protect the feelings of his father – a father that was dead. He must have seen the wasted time flashing by, his own mortality and the unfairness of it all.

I slumped back into my chair, and in that moment felt something I'd never thought possible: sympathy for my father, and a remorse for the life he clearly didn't choose.

Of course he couldn't say: when he was young it was illegal to be gay. Not only that, but he was a footballer, and a footballer in a narrow-minded 1950s northern England. It just wasn't possible for him to come out of the closet in his Sheffield United shirt singing Dusty Springfield songs, and so, like too many others, he'd abandoned the truth for what kept him safe.

I looked at my poor broken sister, sobbing softly to her wine, but still, I couldn't. You can't be sad for something you never had, and he was never mine; he was not my father, I couldn't cry for him.

'Well,' I said, 'we can't go back and change things now. This is where we are, and this is what happens when you bring up your kids on a diet of confusion.'

I took a pause.

'Although, to be perfectly honest, I don't know why he thought he couldn't confide in me. It's not like I've ever conformed to stereotypes, is it? An' apart from all that, he knew how much I loved Larry Grayson.'

Frances forced a smile.

'Yeah,' she said, 'gay Dad. Must be where I get the dress sense.'

'Really? ... Well, if that's the summation of your evidence, then I'm still not convinced. I mean, I never saw him in a cravat.' Then, tugging at her blouse, 'And grey, with your palette?'

***

After that night I began to think of my father in a different way. Yes, he was cruel and took his anger out on his children, but his broken sexuality had morphed into chronic sadness, feigning a lifetime of disguise. Constantly defending himself against his own regrets, he was a man who'd wasted that life, a man who'd rather be dead than be who he was.

Always Paddle In Your Own Canoe

The first day in my new job was quite daunting. Notwithstanding the obvious challenges that lay ahead, I had four things on my mind that particular February morning: my dead father; the fact that I'd borrowed money to buy a second-hand car to get me to a job that paid me less money than I was earning previously; the ongoing debts from my disaster of a marriage; and the dental abscess under a left molar, that had been causing me so much pain, I'd actually decided to pull out my tooth, with only my friend Alice there to render first aid, or to catch me should I faint. I couldn't afford the dentist, and the taste of pure iron from the hole in my mouth was making me nauseous as I drove up the M1 towards Mansfield.

Arriving at Berry Hill, I was enthusiastically received by Barbara, a sparkly little soul, with a happy-clappy smile, and a voice made for porn.

'Hello, Clare,' she gushed. 'How exciting to finally meet you. I've got your office ready, so I'll take you down there now, if that's okay? I'm Barbara by the way.' She held out her tiny hand. She was quite tiny all over, in fact – just five feet tall in her four-inch heels – but still, a very vigorous human being all the same; almost *bouncy* in places.

'Sorry, I'm ... I'm a bit debilitated.' I was carrying my box of tricks: some books on mining and law, oddments of stationery, and a photograph of Evelynne, along with her little pink plant to put on my desk. So I had no other option but to leave Barb the Bounce, now flicking her over-shiny hair from her undersized shoulders, hanging.

'Oh!' she cried. 'I do beg your pardon. Can I help you with that?'

'No, you're alright, I think I can manage.' And as we set off down the corridor, I tried to size her up: what's with the 'beg pardon'? Was she Dickensian?

A few yards on and we finally reached my office. 'Right,' she said, 'make yourself at home and I'll fetch you a drink. Coffee alright?' Her smile now fixed like a happy tattoo on her small, well-meaning face – she was quite irritating.

'Yes, thanks. A coffee would be great.'

And with an unconvincing 'Perfect', off she bounced.

I dropped the box onto the desk and took a good look round. The view was still beautiful, but the room was dark, dank and old-fashioned. Huge empty shelves, fitted integrally to the recess of the wall, loomed heavy to the light, blocking any chance of sun. Which was probably just as well given the burnt-orange 1970s carpet that was neither retro nor kitsch. An old electric heater, with a pre-war appearance and a screech like a B52, sat gurgling its musty warm air, and the smell of mildew, clammy feet and old-lady gussets hung round me like a fog. This was weird. I felt terrorised and more than slightly vulnerable, as the panic of what I'd just done began to set in.

I stood rooted to the floor, trying hard to block the sound of my aggressive inner voice now furiously chatting its negative rant. *Hand me the fucking ration book! Seriously, what the fuck is this? 19-fucking-42?*

I shook my head. Right. What do I need? … What do I need? …

I stood, I thought, I mulled, I agreed. And, with a nod to the murky room, decided to play to the inner budgie and box up the panic instead, by placing my *Mining Six Pack*, *Mines and Quarries Act* and *Judicial Guidelines* on the dusty shelves, in an attempt to effect a more officey-type space. I put Evelynne next to her plant on the desk, and sat back into an old leather chair, trying really hard to raise some power. At which point, the coffee arrived, quickly followed by Mick.

'Hey up, kid, come dine tu my office an' let's have a chat.' He was stood blocking the door, in a dark-grey donkey jacket and a Benny from *Crossroads* hat, with a bucket of strawberry flavoured Slimfast clutched tightly to his chest. 'Chuck one at me an' all, if you don't mind, Beryl.'

'Yes, Mr Stevens.' The tea lady tipped me a wink as I followed him out.

***

Mick's office was a bombsite furnished in the same style as my own, but cluttered with empty mugs, old mining plans, and a mishmash of metal filing cabinets in different shades of green and grey: some chipped, and others without handles or with drawers that didn't close. I got the feeling it really didn't matter to him; he never used them, and besides, if he wanted a file then Barb the Bounce was the man.

'Nythen,' he said, sitting back in his chair, 'I've gen it some thort an' I think we should start by dealing wit lawyers.' A pause. 'Then, praps wi can start dealing wit claims. My view is that wi should handle majority in-house, an' only use them lot as an' when.'

I wasn't quite sure what he meant: there was no 'in-house' to speak of, and from what I could see, he had no staff. Apart from a couple of secretaries, the tea lady and the Bounce, who else was there?

'Reight,' he said, throwing a pile of deafness claims across the desk. 'I've already kept from sendin this lot out. So nye you've finally landed, y'can crack on wi these. Plus, lads fromt pit are comin over later wi some accident forms for you tu look at.'

The tea lady entered the room and, after searching for a vacant coaster, delivered a strong black coffee direct to his eager paw. She pointed to a mountain of dirty mugs. 'D'you want me to take these away, Mr Stevens?'

'Well, they won't tek the sens, will they?'

She rolled her eyes and gathered them up as Mick took a gulp. 'Bloody hell! No bloody sugar!' Then, fumbling in his drawer, he pulled out a small tub of sweeteners, dropping just two into his drink. 'That's better. Now, where were I?'

'Erm, miners and accident claims?'

'Ah, aye, yes. What d'you think, then, Clare?'

'Well, do you have any figures I can look at? That might give me some idea of where we are with the lawyers first and foremost, and then perhaps I can have a look at the claims, and maybe design a system to work with?'

'Aye that's a bloody good idea. I'll get Barbara to put 'em on yer desk.'

'Okay, I'll make a start.' I rose to leave.

'Hang on,' he said. 'How long will that tek?'

I looked at him with some confusion; his impatience was palpable.

'It's just that the bloke who were here before me, previous General Secretary, had a problem wi snuff an' booze, an' I don't know where we are wi it all.'

'Oh, right, well erm … I can work through them this week, and get back to you in a couple of days, if that's alright?'

'A couple o' days?'

'To do it properly, yes.'

'Okay,' he said, with a relieved nod. 'That'll do for me, kid.'

'D'you want me to produce a written report? Something you can refer to at your next meeting?'

'Aye, that'll be great.'

'Right.' I moved to the door and, taking my UDM latte with me, marched back to my office.

Two minutes later, in bounced Barbs with a box full of fee notes, all neatly tied up with pretty pink ribbons. 'There's two more to come,' she sighed. 'I'll bring them down.'

Over the next few days I learnt that the union was in dire financial difficulties, barely able to pay the wages of its handful of employees. There was no infrastructure upon which to build any of the necessary underlying systems of work required for a successful business. The UDM's financial viability and existence, let alone commercial success, were all very uncertain, and this made my position equally uncertain. Still, like I just said, it was too late to start wobbling now. So, burnt-orange carpets, B52s and the smell of old gussets aside, I decided to forge on in my newly acquired Department of Claim, which basically consisted of me and Jackie, whom Mick had allocated to me on a part-time basis.

***

'You've not lived till you've bin on a union school,' said Mick, bellowing from the driver's seat of his Toyota Land Cruiser.

'And after that, you don't want to?'

He gave me the side eye. 'Aye, that's about it.' He smirked.

We were driving to a miners' rest home in Chapel St Leonards, just outside Skegness, where deferred members – usually older retired

151

miners – could book a couple of weeks' respite, which was subsidised by the union.

Mick called it the 'Departure Lounge'. He said, 'Even the windows are bifocal', that it was 'an age-ragers paradise' and 'what happened in respite, stayed in respite'. So, if I saw anything unbecoming, untoward or just downright unsavoury, I was to make like the rest, and keep my big gob shut.

Still, we weren't there for fun. No, we were there to present our business plan to the elected branch secretaries and union officials who ran the union at pit level. Big burly no-nonsense blokes who bawled like bulls, and who, to my complete surprise, were much more amenable to a woman taking the lead than the residents of old FOMTdom town.

They embraced the talk of a bloody good fight, and a bloody good bop to boot, as later that night we all hit Skeg Vegas, and I found myself with twenty dancing partners, a freestyling circle of miner, some of whom were quite nifty movers. Mick was lost in music, and told me that his main hobby in life was disco dancing. The disco-dancing General Secretary was cutting a rug and the last off the floor, still busting a move with the Mud walk, as the DJ packed up for the night.

***

Upon our return, we were ready to distribute the new claim forms to each UDM pit and get cracking with intimating our first few claims against UK Coal, who, to their credit, had already recognised the benefits of dealing with the union directly, not only in terms of legal fees, but also in terms of efficiency.

However, the deafness cases also needed to be addressed, and these cases did not come under the liability of UK Coal. They were in respect of miners who had been made deaf between the years of 1963 and 1990, the year that ear defenders had been made compulsory, and therefore fell under the responsibility of British Coal which, as an old nationalised industry, was now the liability of the Department of Trade and Industry (DTI).

***

I suppose I should have been puking pure adrenalin when we arrived at the office of Martyn Stevens (the DTI's representative on earth). Martyn had been the big boss man when I'd worked at British Coal, operating between Sheffield and London, mostly London, and at ministerial level. So yes, I really should have been puking, but then again, I had just been clubbing in Skegness, and I suppose you could say that my fear had been lost to a certain extent.

As we filed into the conference room, one by one, I could see three members of the negative enforcement brigade sat pushing biscuits into their chubby corporate fizogs. There was: make-mine-a-double Muttley and his increasingly pink face; Gerald the Undynamic, in a signature sweat-stained shirt; and Bottom Line Bob: a slow-moving perennial FOMT, with one eye on the money, and the other on the floor.

'Hey up, lads.' Mick, loud and determined, reached over to shake hands. 'I'm Mick Stevens, General Secretary of UDM. This is Neil Greatrex, Union President. And this young lady, who you no doubt know, is Clare Walker, gamekeeper turned poacher.'

They laughed, but I could see by the whites of their eyes that they were not best pleased that I should be allowed to breathe the same air, never mind attend the same meeting.

'Now, I know you very well, Martyn, and I know you know Neil, but do you know, Clare?' Mick pointed his big purple index finger right at my small head, just in case any of the six men in the room were unsure who 'Clare' was.

Martyn looked at me and smiled. He was genuinely a very nice, level-headed, intelligent man, who deserved to be in a senior position. People respected him, mainly because he respected them. Neither condescending, nor braggish, Martyn was a gentleman.

'Yes,' he said. 'I know Clare very well. She was Student of the Year.' He leant in and shook my hand. 'Nice to see you again.' Then, turning to Mick, whispered, 'You've taken one of my best.' And with that, we all sat down.

'Right,' said Mick, straight to the point as usual. 'What it is, is that we as a union have to mek some sort on alternative funding if we're gonna survive.' He reached into his jacket, pulling out his trusty tube of sweeteners, dropping a now mandatory two into his cup. 'An' the reason Clare's come tu wok for us is that we want tu set up us own claims department where we tek place ont lawyers in most cases, an' you as defendant pay us a fee for bringin a case, rather than being hung out tu dry wi solicitors costs.' He paused. 'An' we get to mek some money fot union. Wi pit closures an' the like, membership's dwindling an' we need to exist in tut future.' He sat back, looking at the FOMTs one by one. I could tell he felt quite proud, not just of his speech, but of the concept. I'd started to understand him much more, recently. I listened to what he meant, rather than what he said: he wasn't the most articulate man on the planet, but he certainly knew what he wanted as far as the union was concerned.

'Well, there's no objection here, Mick.' Martyn was leaning back in his chair. 'In fact, we've done some homework on the average cost of an average solicitor, and if you can come in lower than that, then we're happy to have an agreement in place. Obviously, now the DTI is taking over the liability of British Coal, it's important that we attempt to save as much taxpayers' money as possible.'

I felt I had to say something. I didn't want to sit there looking like a doll's head, and so ... 'Yes, we've done some of that research too.'

Mick shot me a side glance. I could read his expression: it was saying, 'Did we?'

'And while we can hold the majority of cases in-house we will, of course, still need to refer cases out, to a preferred list of panel firms.'

'Which cases?' Martyn leant forward, coaxing a response.

'Well, those that are complex medically, such as severe tinnitus, and those that may become the subject of litigation. Obviously, not being a firm of solicitors, we can't actually issue proceedings. Then there's the under-ten-decibel cases, and mining contractors, that sort of thing.'

'Why contractors?'

'Because they might not agree to pay their proportion of our costs.'

'Ah, see what y'mean.' He stroked his beard. But I knew, that he knew, that I knew that he knew the issues very well indeed and, being on a big fat roll, I decided to continue.

'The union puts the miner first, but also needs proper recompense for its efforts. The new government White Paper on Modernising Justice recommends that representing bodies such as unions should be allowed to bring claims for those they represent, but such organisations will not get involved unless they are fairly remunerated. Further, if we can sit down like reasonable adults and agree a list of preferred consultants to undertake the medical testing, then we at the union can also tie those consultants into a fixed rate for medical reports, making savings in terms of disbursements, as well as costs, for the DTI to consider when protecting the public purse.' I drew breath. 'After all, there really is no point in us obtaining a medical report from a consultant you can't accept; you'd have to get your own, and we'd attempt to negotiate between the two, then we might have to get a third, or further comments, all of which raises the costs to your DTI and causes unnecessary delays to the miners in getting the compensation they deserve.'

There was complete silence.

The FOMTs sat open-mouthed.

'Bloody hell,' said Mick. 'Talk about bring a tear tu yer granny's glass eye. I were almost choked mi sen.'

Martyn laughed. 'Indeed. I told you she was one of my best.'

'Aye, I think you might be right, Martyn. In fact, we went tut union school last week, an' she got best compliment I've ever heard a miner gee anyone. This lad from Harworth said, "Clare Walker, she's dog's bollocks". They all want her tu handle their claims. They'd gu bloody mad if wi passed um on tut lawyers.'

The use of the 'B' word hadn't seemed like an issue for anyone else in the meeting, certainly not Martyn, who was a bit of a right-on liberal. I imagined him on his days off in a pair of clogs, smoking roll-ups, drinking real ale and operating some sort of loom, while morris dancing in his Ban-the-Bomb T-shirt and friendship bangles. Yes, he was the full lentil, a bit of a hippy, but still, longsighted and sensible – a consummate professional.

So, after a long, drawn-out meeting, bartering on the price of claims, consultants and the adverse costs of litigation, we finally reached an agreement to handle claims for industrial deafness.

Martyn asked if the union had any intention of handling claims for chest diseases and VWF. He made it clear that the DTI would welcome the union with open arms and an open handling agreement if the union should decide to intimate their cases direct, rather than outsourcing the work to lawyers.

I'd just shot Mick a look that said, 'Shut the fuck up right now. Don't say a fucking word', when Neil Greatrex, a man who up until now had remained silent, opened his mouth and said, 'Tha needs tu get us in t'see minister. We aint gerrin involved in any more on this claims shit till we know how it's gonna affect union.'

I hadn't understood why he'd been there until then, and in just one sentence, all came clear. Mick only wheeled out Neil when there was someone who needed a good shouting down, swearing at or threatening. A sort of good cop, bad cop arrangement, which might have been appropriate if we'd all been starring in an episode of *The Sweeney*, but we weren't, and I really wanted to punch him on the end of his half-nibbled nose.

***

Needless to say, a few weeks later, Mick and I were on the train to London for a meeting with the DTI. I'd prepared the usual time-spent figures in order to secure our costs, making sure they were completely reasonable and above criticism. I'd taken a very curt phone call from smarm-merchant Muttley earlier that week, culminating in, 'I doubt the department would want to deal with the UDM direct. Let's face it, the union's a complete political leper, and your President appears to be a thug in a suit, so forget any handling agreement cos you won't bloody well get it!'

I imagined his face to be as scarlet as a postbox, as he slammed down the phone, denying me a right to reply.

The Large Print Giveth

As Mick and I sat in reception at 1 Victoria Street, slap bang in Government Central, it suddenly dawned on me just how far we'd come from what had started out as a money-saving exercise just a few months before.

We were meeting with government officials, and on the cusp of two Claims-Handling Agreements, arising from two of the biggest pieces of litigation ever to be heard in Europe, and quite possibly, the world.

'This could be huge for the union, Mick. We've really got to make sure we don't start effing and jeffing today.' I was looking at his bus driver's tie, the one with the UDM logo he'd snatched from the display cabinet in reception earlier that day, having forgotten to bring one of his own.

'Don't panic, lass. It's not me thas got tu worry about. It's Neil. He's a c**t and nine bits wi his bleedin an' fuckin – that's a real bloody problem.'

Neil wasn't here. What in the name of golden hell was he talking about? And apart from that, had he heard himself?

'Reight, nythen, while I remember, av you got them forms?'

'Sorry?'

'Claim forms!'

'Erm, oh yes, yes … sorry.' I took them from my briefcase and pushed them into his hand. 'Right, as you can see they're both very similar in the way they wheedle out personal details, but I've made the work histories specific to the claim-type, and the medical symptoms too.'

'Why's that?' He was trying to loosen the tie, which appeared to be cutting the blood supply to his head.

'Because to suffer from VWF, you have to have used handheld vibration tools in your occupation from January 1975, and present with certain symptoms.'

'Like?' It really wasn't budging.

'Like tingling and numbness, loss of dexterity, and loss of colour, commonly known as blanching. Not only that, but only certain occupations may be able claim; that is, those miners who actually used handheld vibration tools on a daily basis, so most surface men may well be barred. We just don't know yet and won't really know until the framework to the scheme is up and running.' I could see he was only borderline alert.

'An' what's details wi bronchitis?' He gave up on the tie, attempting to open his top button instead.

'Well,' said I, trying to draw breath, 'the term Chronic Obstructive Pulmonary Disease is a generic term for claimable diseases, and under this umbrella the claimable diseases for miners are currently said to be bronchitis, emphysema and exacerbation of asthma. You have to have been exposed to dust and fumes from June 1954 in your occupation as a miner to be eligible to make a claim, and just for completeness I've done a claims profile on how many claims we expect to receive for each disease, based on current claimable jobs and occupations.' I handed him the figures in a blue plastic folder, and held his stare, which by now was totally blank.

'Is that bloody paint drying behind you?' He laughed. 'You bleedin borin twat! It's a good job Neil's not bleedin well here.'

'Indeed. We wouldn't want a potty mouth lowering the tone, would we? But trust me, you'll thank me for this one day.' I put my fist to his face and he took the folder.

'To be honest, mate, I could do wi a coffee. I had a bit too much red wine last night, an' mi bleedin head's bangin.'

I checked my bag for aspirin. 'Well, yes, tannic headaches are the price you pay for enjoying a full-bodied red.'

He paused for a moment, slightly irritated, and then, 'What's bleedin *Titanic* got tu do wi owt?'

Just then, a short, moist little man, with greasy shoulder-length hair, bearing an uncanny resemblance to a tango instructor trotting the boards of the 'bleedin *Titanic*', approached us. 'Hello. Mick and Clare?' he enquired, in a surprisingly high-pitched voice.

Mick held out his hand and threw him a wink. 'Aye,' he said. 'She's Mick and I'm Clare.'

Unfortunately, tiny dancer, whose security pass looked nothing like him, didn't get the joke and, turning his back, snapped, 'This way, please!'

We followed him through a security gate, where Mick remarked that I should be careful not to set the metal detectors off with the wires in my jaw. I told him that, in reality, it was more likely to be the metal plate in his head, or the dog-shaped novelty cufflinks he'd taken to wearing of late. Again, tight-lipped-tetchy-tango-tits failed to find the funny. So, taking the hint, we picked up the pace and followed on in silence.

Through the glass doors, down a glass corridor, in a glass lift, then out again, across the open-plan, past all the glass people and their bifold world to a boardroom built for battle, where our humourless chaperone, with a face like an angry alpaca, knocked lightly on the door. 'The UDM,' he squeaked.

And, as the room opened up, I felt the rush of panic that told me I was out of my depth. The sweat cracked down my back and I heaved a dry wretch. *What the hell was I doing here? Who did I think I was?*

I stood rooted to the floor, staring into the abyss – a terrifying chasm of mahogany, pinstripes, notepads, and water coolers. I looked at Mick, and he at me, as we drew a synchronised breath and walked in.

Now, it has to be said there is no stranger creature on the planet than the average government official. Walking into the boardroom was a bit like sitting down to negotiate with the cast of *Misshapen Heads of the World, Part Three – Does Anyone Have a Heartbeat?*

From the miners' strike to pit closures, from windy picks to pneumoconiosis X-ray data, it was now very clear that the department was more than desperate to deal with the UDM. The solicitors' group representing the other two miners' unions were not, as one official put it, 'Moving quickly to resolve issues', and were, as the DTI saw it, 'Simply running up costs and causing unnecessary delays to the claimant by taking the adversarial line'.

I'm not sure what the government expected. Like us, the solicitors' group were fighting for the rights of their miners. They were hardly going to lay down and accept everything the government wanted – that's not how damage and compensation worked.

'The only issue we have,' said Mick, chucking two more

sweeteners into his cup of black coffee, 'is mekkin sure that we all ger heard, strike or no bloody strike.'

I cut in. 'You see, to us, a sick miner is a sick miner. It doesn't really matter what tribe he belongs to.'

I could feel this strike a chord with the DTI who, at the very least, wanted to be *seen* to be fair and equitable.

'All we want,' said Mick, wincing at the coffee, 'is a fair deal fot miners, an' a fair deal fot union. I've sed it time an' time agen.' And he had. 'It's no good tut union if miners aren't looked after. We don't have shareholders, but we do have members, an' as long as nowt upsets cart wi them ...' He was fumbling around for yet another sweetener, and had lost his thread, so I cut him off.

'Okay. I've spent some time recording costs on a cross section of files, in order that we can come to some agreement for a set fee, one which mirrors the ongoing negotiations you're having with the solicitors' group.' I passed copies of my figures across the shiny desk.

'Right,' said half-man, half-dolphin, Bob Shore, a senior civil servant (who wouldn't have looked too out of place jumping hoops in an entertainment aquarium, having his teeth cleaned with an oversized toothbrush), scanning the numbers for a non-existent fault.

'Although we are aware you will need to pass everything through the Public Accounts Committee, we also understand that, as claims handlers, we can only claim costs in the region of 83.33 per cent of those made by solicitors.' I was quoting the government White Paper again, throwing their words back in their faces. 'As you can see from the attached, we come in under that.'

'I see,' said Bottlenose Bob. 'And do we have an estimation of the expected number of claims?'

'Well, let's bat that one back to you, Bob. How many d'you expect?' questioned Mick, cocky of voice and ready for a fight. 'Countrywide, o' course.'

He looked at Mick with a marked indifference. 'For VWF? Well, the department's crunched some numbers, and we think that somewhere in the region of 30,000 miners may be eligible to claim. I can't really speak for COPD, but we don't expect those figures to exceed that current projection either.'

Mick nearly chocked on his coffee, which by now had four sweeteners swimming around its black consistency. 'Thirty thousand? Thirty bloody thousand? I dunt know where thas got them figures from, but whoever's gen 'em thee wants sacking! There's oer 60,000 in our region alone!'

Bob seemed more than a little embarrassed at having the idiot lamp shone on him and, with his rostrum slightly out of joint, was just about to respond when Mick, unable to read his emotion, continued his smack in the blowhole. 'Nythen, before I let dog off lead,' (he was thumb-pointing me, I was the dog), 'she's done her research, an' you're way out, Bob ... way out. She's gorrall facts, an' what can speak can't bloody well lie.' He was shaking his head in order to drum the shout home.

And with my muzzle finally gone, I was indeed off the lead. 'Yes, like Mick said, we've done some figures on the expected number of claims within each occupational group, and also completed a full claims profile for your digestion on those claims currently registered at the UDM. Additionally, we are aware that the Claims-Handling Agreement for VWF is almost ready to be signed off with the solicitors' group, and that the COPD agreement won't be far behind, so we'd be grateful if you could give this your urgent attention.'

'Aye.' Mick was back in the game, having given up on the coffee. 'We've got oer 30,000 already. An' wi might end up havin tu send em *all* tut lawyers, who'll no doubt want tu charge full price. I don't think taxpayers will be too happy about that one, Bob.'

Now he was really dissing him, and in his own hood! Mick was so bonkers that, on occasion, he actually backed into genius, and this was one such occasion. The power of our negotiation was always going to be proportionate to the number of claims we held.

But Bob was raking his teeth. He wasn't happy and, with our costs tucked tightly under his flipper, swam off, in a swarming shoal of junior porpoises, sporting wry, suck-it-up beaks, as they scuttled out behind their leader.

I sat myself back for what was fast becoming the obligatory two minutes silence.

Blimey, I didn't know about Bob, but even I felt slightly insulted as I scanned the empty seats, the shiny leather notepads and freshly sharpened pencils that, like the tiny bottles of water, were neither opened nor used.

'Well,' I said, 'look on the bright side: if we don't get what we want, it won't be for a lack of charm … or lip gloss, will it?'

Mick shook his head and, never knowingly out-nuttered, threw a purple thumb their way. 'Y'can't educate pork, Clare. Now, is there anywhere we can gerra proper coffee? I can't drink this shit.'

***

Over the next few weeks my time was spent in talks with the DTI and their accountant, Mr Wildgoose-Perkins, another stray from the land of rude, who didn't do smiling, or people for that matter, and appeared to expect that everyone answering his calls would, for some insane reason, know immediately who he was. No greet, just straight into the forensics of time-spent, fee notes and VAT.

His phones calls were duller than a party political broadcast. He mashed my brain to a pulp with his monosyllabic grunts and quantitative teasing, so much so that I seriously considered downing half a pint of Harpic with a baby aspirin chaser after each and every encounter.

Finally, once the slippery issue of costs had been successfully negotiated, they had to be passed to, and approved by, the Public Accounts Committee.

This process seemed to take forever until both Claims Handling Agreements were eventually signed off and we could get on with the task of obtaining compensation for our miners.

We had managed to secure significantly more for the union than Muttley had told me we had any right to expect. He'd been sticking his crimson snout into negotiations all the way, making it difficult for anyone to progress into any sort of meaningful debate and, after being dragged through the public accounts hedge backwards, I felt a real need to twat him right between his smug, sexist and increasingly bloodshot eyes. So, I sent him ten thousand claims, a UDM tea towel and a shiny pink note that read:

Dear Muttley,

Thanks for the input, but not everyone wants to catch the pigeon, or chlamydia for that matter, and I certainly don't want to be saved.

Kindest regards,

Penelope Poundcoin.

PS Sometimes Barbie wins x

***

After the signing-off of the Handling Agreements, I went headbanging down into a Bachman-Turner (you ain't seen nothing yet) overdrive, devising and implementing the systems that were to eventually form the foundations of the claims-handling operations of the union.

To meet the demand for claims, we took on more and more claims staff, which meant we could hit the ground running in all aspects of the claims-handling process. Much investment was made in IT and I worked with programmers to write systems designed specifically to deal with industrial disease. We set up information desks and call centres, and ran numerous training courses, inviting guest speakers – such as respiratory specialists, ear, nose and throat surgeons, vascular surgeons, solicitors, barristers and others – to train staff on medical, legal and other specialised issues. The mantra was, if you understood the medical, you understood the claim.

And we didn't stop at claims: we also set up three, state-of-the-art medical testing centres, in a groundbreaking, one-stop industrial disease shop at the UDM offices, Berry Hill Lane.

We had biweekly policy meetings with the DTI in London and worked hand in hand with the department to achieve the very best for our miners, the numbers of which were rising, making the UDM the biggest claims-handling organisation at that time.

The UDM, a nimble learning organisation, had gone out into the communities, making contact with the miners and their families, offering them a first-class claims service: one they understood, expected and deserved.

However, this success was not without criticism from various organisations. In fact, the politics of the situation was perhaps the one thing I hadn't fully grasped. I hadn't considered for one moment how much the success of the UDM would affect and infect its enemies.

But ordinary working people are not as unenlightened as most members of the political class would like to believe and, instead of being deterred, more and more miners began to vote with their feet, by coming to the UDM to make their claims.

In short, we were kicking the establishment firmly between the legs, holding it up to be inefficient and out of touch, shining a light on its industry, and finding it wanting. More than able to stand our ground, we didn't need to work with those so set against us in any event. We could develop our own strategy for handling our own claims, always negotiating our own specific points and fighting our own corner on the issues of equity and fairness. And, as the poet Mick Stevens so eloquently put it:

'They can call us what they bloody well want, Clare. Two dogs fuckin for all I care. I'd rather shit on mi hands an' clap, then work wi them lot.'

Treat It Like a Moment

A three-year period of a fourteen-hour day, seven days a week, fast-forward work schedule had finally turned me into a human spreadsheet. My particular style of tunnel-vision work placement meant I had no time for friends or, more to the point, any friends I *did* have were usually those I worked with, so when my secretary put a call through from my ex-husband, I was glad to have some contact with the outside world.

'Hello, you. It's me. How you diddling? Still the Doris Day of deep-mining, I presume?' His voice was refreshing and familiar.

'That's right, up to my twinky twinset in work, too busy to laugh, but lovin it all the same.' Blimey, what a yawn merchant of the flipping snorefest I was, with my rip-roaring fetish for all things coal. Seriously, did anyone outwith the hamster wheel of claim really give a shit? No, of course they didn't, because they had a life.

'Wow,' he said. 'Sounds complex.'

'Yes, yes. I'm very important. So get on with it … what d'you want?'

'I'm in need of a chat. D'you think we can meet?'

'Course we can, why? What's up?'

'Well, it's a bit … difficult to be honest, and I'd rather not discuss it over the phone.'

'Oh, okay …' Now I was checking my diary. It was booked solid for the next few weeks with absolutely no gaps. My lunches were always working lunches with one firm or another. I'd have to cancel something and squeeze him in, maybe between the Glenfield Respiratory Unit and the meeting with the minister next week in London? I scanned the pages, trying to find a way, when …

'It's really important, hun, I really do need to see you.'

'Right. Well, I can certainly do next Monday? Or if that's no good, what about this Friday?' I loved Fridays, not because it was the end of the working week, because for me it wasn't – I worked most weekends. My love of Friday stemmed from childhood, when Evelynne allowed us our weekly bar of chocolate, every Friday night after tea. She called it 'Friday treat'.

'Saturday would be better.' He was more than insistent. 'I can come to Sheffield on the train and meet you in town if you like?'

Saturday? That was my catch-up on the 10,000 emails day; the day I could sit in my office, read mining, breathe mining, eat, sleep and flipping well drink mining … Saturday – really?

I thought about it. 'Okay,' I conceded. 'I'll see you Saturday outside the Crucible, at one-ish? It'll be good to catch up. Play your cards right, an' I might even buy lunch.'

'Lunch? We haven't done that in a long time. Lunch sounds good.' His voice was breaking, so I snatched the conversation back.

'Okay, no worries. I'll see you Saturday. Looking forward to it.'

'Yeah, see you then, then.'

I wasn't quite sure what all the wobbling was about, but I got the distinct feeling that Saturday wasn't exactly going to be a funsters' day out.

***

Sitting on the wall outside the Crucible Theatre, I could feel the soothing warmth of the sun on my back and, watching the people walk by, it suddenly dawned on me just how long it'd been since I'd spent a sunny afternoon on the Sheffield Riviera. My office in Mansfield was the place I seemed to spend all my time, when not in London, of course, arm-wrestling with government ministers and officials.

From my position, I could see the bank building where, in the dark days of Bucket Fanny Gate, I'd been refused as little as twenty English pounds by an incredibly abrasive junior manger, a one-size-fits-all-deep-fried-corporate, with a face as tight as a knot, who'd said, 'It's no longer in the bank's interest to allow you any more money. We've just received your wages and you're already £60 overdrawn'.

'Well,' I'd responded, tears of despair beginning to make their way down my cheeks, 'that's why I wanted to ask for an agreed overdraft … so … so that I can get back on my feet a little at a time, and—'

'I'm sorry,' she spat, cutting in, cutting me off and cutting me down. 'With a collection of County Court Judgments like that, we're not really in a position to allow a bigger overdraft and you're not really in a position to negotiate.' And with that, she was up, in her flat, black, regulation-twat shoes, ushering me up and off the chair, marching me at speed past an oversized poster of a smiling, post-menopausal woman, complete with handsome husband, dressed in millionaire-caramel cashmere, reclining on expensive-looking garden furniture, accompanied by the future generations of family, all shiny self-love, pensions and savings, before pushing me firmly out of the glass doors and onto the street.

I'd walked the eight miles home that night crying most of the way, vowing to take my overdraft elsewhere at the first available opportunity.

I shuddered at the thought of just how bad things had been in the Pot Noodle sandwich period of my life and was glad that I'd managed to put that painful chapter behind me and move on, treat it as a moment, not a monument.

Now, sitting here on the wall, I was pleased Tony and I had managed to stay friends, and could meet on a sunny Saturday for lunch and a quick catch-up at Cue's café.

However, my relief was short-lived. From the approach, I could see by his face that he hadn't come for a jaunty lunch, but to deliver bad news; the kind I really hadn't expected.

He told me that he'd developed a brain tumour, which for some reason (he wasn't clear) couldn't be removed.

'It's benign,' he said, staring into his cup, 'and slow-growing, so we're just going to see how things develop, keep it monitored with regular check-ups.'

I reached out and took his hand. 'I'm so sorry. I don't know what to say.'

He squeezed my fingers. 'It's okay, kid. I just needed to tell someone. Y'know, talk it through. I haven't even told my mother yet. I need some time to think before I start having any difficult conversations with her.'

I knew his mother well; she wasn't exactly backwards at coming forwards. Her type of motherly love was more contact sport than nurture; she could shake a seven on the emotional spectrum and I knew he didn't have the mindset to face it right now. So I made a promise to keep his secret, as we ate our lunch and delicately switched the subject between us.

Late into the afternoon, we took our walk back down to the station and hugged a long goodbye. 'I don't want to die,' he whispered.

'Don't be daft, you won't die. Really you won't. You'll get through this.' And, squeezing him ever tighter, kissed his cheek as he left for the train, no longer able to drive due to his diagnosis and the seizures that had become a side effect of the tumour.

I drove away reviewing the lunchtime conversation as worry began to set in. I knew my ex-husband better than most. I got the feeling there was more to Tony's illness than he was prepared to admit, to me or to himself. I'd seen that look before: anxiety and avoidance. It was in his eyes, there was the whiff of a half-story, something he wasn't saying. Yes, I knew him well, and he was definitely playing it down.

***

December was always a difficult month, and after the Christmas break we'd return to the office to find that many of our claimants had passed away. We had some elderly miners who, already severely disabled by a progressive respiratory disease, had been further weakened by the cold weather, unable to fight off the infections and viruses that winter brought. There'd be a sharp rise in deaths come January.

On this particular day, I was in reply to Mr Ballswing's (probably not his real name) monthly 'Beware of the nasty spider web covering this now pagan planet' letter, which he sent to me, Nelson Mandela, Queen Elizabeth II, the European Parliament, Michael Bentine, Tony Blair and someone called Glug … in that order. I always wrote back, and had just enveloped my reply when I was pleasantly disturbed.

'I've got an offer for Pharo Fudge!' said Ruthie, as she burst through the partition between my office and the Claims Department.

Ruthie was my favourite Claims Manager, and Pharo Fudge was her favourite claimant. We'd always been amazed that his mother had sought to call him Pharo, when his brother was called something slightly more traditional, like 'Brian'. Pharo Fudge. He made Madonna sound like Steve.

'That's great.' I looked up from my screen that told me I had fifty-seven new emails, most of them policy changes to the Claims Handling Agreements received from the DTI. 'How much is it?'

'Not enough,' she said, her eyes scanning the schedule of special damages. 'They've misinterpreted the medical report for a start, and haven't included his pension loss or taken into account that he also has a diagnosis of bronchitis.' She hit the letter using the back of her hand, as if to pronounce the nonsense.

'Best get on to them straightaway and get them to revise it.' I shook my head. 'And tell them we'd like it before *next* Christmas, if at all possible!'

'Ha, yeah!' She laughed, still studying the schedule of losses, as she walked slowly back to her desk. Then, returning for further comment, stuck her head back round the door. 'Yes, and they've used a smoking factor of *heavy*, when his GP notes clearly state light!'

'Swindling bastards! Tell 'em to stick it up their useless backsides! And do it in writing – without prejudice, of course.'

'Indeed,' she said. 'I'll enjoy the sport.' And with that, she was off.

I settled back into my chair, thinking very proud thoughts of my perfect little team. They were very good at their jobs: competent and aggressive in their pursuit of a good settlement, which is exactly how they had to be if we were going to get the best offers.

At that moment, my secretary barged her way in. 'Clare, I know you're busy, but could you talk to this lady in reception? She's really upset and she's asking for you.'

'What's her name?' Still half-reading policy amendment 17 to section 6, paragraph 4.

'Alice Green. She said her husband's called Vernon?'

I looked up. 'Vernon ... Vernon? Oh, *Vernon*! Yes, I'll come straight out.'

I followed her out of the office and down the corridor to

reception, where a very small worried-looking woman was sat waiting with a UDM letter clutched tightly in her fist.

'Hello, you were asking for me? I'm Clare Walker.' I smiled and held out my hand as she, in turn, collapsed into tears. It was 10.00 a.m. and reception was filling with forms, claimants, doctors and staff. It was far too busy an environment for such a vulnerable woman, so I put my arm around her shoulders and ushered her to my office instead.

This was a scene I knew well. Over the years there had been many miners' widows, daughters and sons taking tea and advice in my office. Sometimes after the death, sometimes before: all difficult and emotionally fraught times. I understood the meaning of loss, so I took my seat next to Alice, as she began.

'I've come about mi husband's claim. His name's Vernon, he said he knows you from a long time ago?' She searched my face for confirmation.

'Yes, that's right. He worked at the pit I used to investigate.'

'Well, now he's retired, due to ill-health wi his chest, an' had that report done wit doctors who made him breath in tut tube?' She fiddled for her handkerchief.

'Yes, his medical assessment for bronchitis and emphysema.'

'Eye, well somebody from your office sent it for him to agree, an' spoke to him over't phone to explain how it'd affect his claim, like ...' Grasping the hanky in her tiny fist, she quickly dried her eyes; a cue for my reply.

'Yes, we do that because the medical reports can be hard to understand. They need explaining properly.'

'Well,' she said, wiping her nose, 'can you just explain what that hundred per cent thing means? It sez he's a hundred per cent disabled, and I ... here,' she said, opening her bag, 'I've gorrit wi me. Can you just gu through it? Just so I know?'

'The thing is, Alice, unless I have Vernon's permission, I can't. I'm not allowed to talk to anyone other than Vernon, unless he's signed something to allow me to talk to you. I really can't. I'm sorry.'

'Oh, dear.' She was getting even more upset now.

'Tell you what ... what if I give you a lift home and, if he's okay with it, I can explain the report to you both at the same time. Would that help?'

'Yes,' she said, 'that'd be great.'

'Okay, we'll have a drink and then we'll get off. Now, where's that tea?'

***

Alice and I arrived at Chez Vernon about 11.30 that morning. Upon entering the tiny terraced house I could hear the familiar wisp of an oxygen tank and, as we walked into the front room, I was shocked to see a thinner, somewhat truncated Vernon to that of old, sitting quietly in his chair between the window and the bed, where he apparently spent most of his days, just watching the world go by.

Pulling the oxygen mask from his face, he shot me a huge smile. 'Hey up, lass. How's tha doin?'

I put my arms around his neck and kissed his head. 'Better than you, by the looks of it.'

'Ah, it's all for show, Clare. Nowt wrong wi me, really.'

'Well,' I smiled, 'I've come to go through your medical report anyway. Alice was getting worried and I wanted to put her mind at rest.'

He looked at his wife. You could see the love between them. They'd married at just eighteen years old and had four children: three boys – none of them miners – and one girl, who, just married, was pregnant with her first child.

'She werries, that's all, Clare. I've told her there's nowt tu werret about.'

I looked into his eyes. We both knew there was; there was lots to worry about. Things did not look good for him.

We sat down to more tea and I began to explain how the doctor had come to his diagnosis. Vernon had never smoked, which was a rarity. Smoking and coal dust share a common pathway when it comes to emphysema, in that they are both a cause, and the damage inflicted by either cannot be separated.

Around eighty per cent of miners during the 1950s, 60s and 70s smoked and, given that British Coal was not liable for any damage caused by smoking, this had to be deducted from the claim. But Vernon, a non-smoker, had been solely disabled by the tortious dust he'd breathed in while working as a miner. He was a strong man, a healthy man, but this equal-opportunities disease had felled him like the lint of a tree.

'Y'see, Clare, Alice is worried that it sez I'm a hundred per cent disabled at age sixty, an' then ... nowt. An' bugger me, I'm sixty-two now!' He started to laugh, but the wheezing took over. Try as he might, he couldn't fight it off, and nearly choked his last breath as he sat in his chair. Alice sprang to her feet and, placing the mask over his face, eased him back onto the pillows that were propping him up. He winked me a nod. His eyes said it all: retirement was a luxury that time would no longer afford, but he needed Alice to hold to faith and me to cushion the blow.

'Carry on,' he mumbled, 'carry on.'

'Okay,' I said. 'Alice, it's really important that you don't get too hung up on the disability grid by over-focusing on the one hundred per cent thing. This is the age at which the doctor estimates that Vernon could be totally disabled, in that he will need full-time care and assistance. But it's not an exact science; in fact it's more guesstimate than estimate, and the rating can be affected by many factors. At the end of the day, it all comes down to your living environment and the quality of care you receive.'

I could see Vernon got the best care from Alice. The house was spotless and she cleaned it twice a day, just to keep down the dust she knew would affect his breathing. No one was allowed to smoke anywhere near the house, and with his bed now positioned in the front room he didn't even have to struggle getting in and out of the stairlift they'd had fitted just two years before.

'But what about this, then, Clare?' She was pointing to the life-expectancy column, which Vernon had already surpassed.

I looked at her poor worn-out expression and, giving an honest answer to a very difficult question, said: 'The thing is, you can outlive the estimated life expectancy. It is, after all, just an opinion. In fact, we've discussed this very issue many times with the DTI, because many miners are actually living way beyond the diagnosis of their projected life expectancy.'

'Ah well,' said Vernon, taking the mask from his face once more and squeezing his wife by the hand. 'I've got the best. It's like havin mi own private nurse. Anythin I want, she'll allus get.'

Alice smiled. 'Thanks, Clare. That's been really helpful. Right,' she said, gathering up the cups, ' I'll just get these washed.'

'Would you like me to dry?' I asked, following her into the kitchen.

'If you don't mind.' She threw me a tea towel, and donning the Marigolds, ran some piping-hot water into a yellow plastic bowl. 'Really, thanks for that, Clare. It's good of you to have come all this way.'

'Not at all, glad to help. Besides, it's nice to get out of the office.'

'An' I'm glad that it's you that's doin his claim an' all.'

'Yeah, about that,' I quizzed, with a side glance. 'Why *did* Vernon choose the UDM to handle his claim? It's just that when he was at the pit, he was NUM through and through. He still had Coal-Not-Dole stickers on his snap tin. I would've thought the UDM was the last place he'd have gone.'

'Ah,' she smiled, squeezing the Fairy Liquid. 'I wondered when you were gonna ask that one. Now, that is what you might call a long story.'

'It's alright, I've got plenty of time.'

'Okay. Well, it all started wi his brother.'

'His brother? Vernon had a brother?'

'He did. His brother was called Frank.' She let out a chuckle. 'I know, hard to fathom int it, that there might av been two on 'em. Anyway, Frank worked at Bilsthorpe, and he were quite active int union, particularly at pit level. 'Course, when Scargill called strike, he came straight out, just like Vernon. But after a few weeks, he had a bit of a falling out wit national executive. Y'see, Frank had a thing about union rules, an' a strong belief in one man, one vote: that everything union did should be democratic an' fair, looking out fot working miner. It were a closed shop in them days, an' he were adamant that leadership should listen tut membership at all times, particularly when it came to major issues like striking.' She grabbed the scourer and started to scrub the inside of Vernon's 'Bestest Dad' mug.

'But Scargill still refused 'em national ballot, so Frank picked 'em up wit rule book, said he dint pay his membership to be tret like a twat!' She rolled her eyes. 'An' although he were really mad wi 'em then, it wern't til Notts Union decided to ignore national union an' have a district vote, that Frank really took umbrage.'

She turned, carefully placing the mug on the drainer. 'So off he went, tut district ballot an' gen his vote. 'Course, Frank voted tu strike, but majority voted against it. So accepting majority's decision, he went back tu work.'

I picked up the mug and started to dry. 'He went back? Back to work?'

'Yes, Clare, he went back to work. Said he'd come out on strike when Scargill allowed all paid-up members their rights nationally, an' if majority voted to strike, he'd go wit vote. But till then, only vote they'd bin gen had gone against um. 'Course, then when they sent flying pickets tu force um out, Frank got more and more determined he were gonna work. Dint bother him that they called him a scab. He'd turn round an' shout "Ballots!"

'But it did bother Vernon. He couldn't stand it, y'see, Clare. He watched Frank get kicked about by't pickets. They stood outside his house, bricked his windows; his wife were called McGregor's Whore and his kids were smacked at school. It got really bad.' She placed another cup upside down on the drainer for me to dry. 'It dam near brok Vern's heart, but he just cun't forgive him. There were no way Vern were goin back, ballot or no ballot, he were wit grass-pie brigade.' She took a sharp breath in and sighed her disappointment. 'Although he never called Frank, he did cut him off, like he never even existed. And after Frank moved away, we never heard from him agen, an' Vern never mentioned him agen either.'

'That must have been really hard on Vernon. Everyone came out at his pit, didn't they?'

'They certainly did.'

'He must have been really embarrassed.' I knew from working at British Coal that the union essentially ran the pit. It would have been a tar-and-feathering offence to strike-break at a pit closed by the strike, ballot or no ballot.

'Yeah, Vern were mortified by it all, but that's not end on it.' She went to the kitchen door, closing it gently so as not to wake Vernon, who was drifting to a snooze.

'Frank died just after Vern took ill-health retirement, an' he were devastated when he eventually found out. We all were. But Vern dint even get a chance tut gu tut funeral, because he dint know. He dint find out Frank were dead till he were told two months later at Welfare by Frank's wife's brother, Ray. He were also very strong wit union: NUM tut core, a bit like Vern, although Ray spent most ont strike travelling up an' down coalfields wit flying pickets, shagging women en route. Elaine, his wife, would've knocked him in tut middle on next week if she'd found out.' She shook her head. 'Anyway, Ray were right smug: told Vern that Frank were dead, then shouted at top on his voice: "Anyway, Vern, once a scab always a scab!" An' that's when we ended up int County Court, after Vernon punched his lights out, right then an' there int middle on Welfare!'

She gave a heavy sigh. 'Honestly, Clare, he could've bloody well killed him.'

'That must have been such dreadful news for Vernon, though.'

'It nearly broke him. All them years, an' for what?' She reached up and opened the cupboard door. 'That's it, y'see: that strike, it split brother from brother, father from sons, tore families apart, sometimes forever. Feelings ran very deep. There were a lot of bitterness … still is.'

It was true. Feelings had run deep, as Alice had put it, and many families had been blown apart by the toxic fallout of the miners' strike, caught as they were between a rock (Thatcher) and a hard place (Scargill) – two political giants fighting out their discordant differences in the coalfields of Britain.

Thatcher knew a fight with the miners was coming and, as a precaution, had stored up tons and tons of surplus coal, in readiness for a long drawn-out battle.

Unfortunately, Scargill called a strike without a national ballot, and used flying pickets to force working miners to join the strike instead.

By doing so, not only did he play directly into the hands of Thatcher, he also split the union by underestimating the power and belief in democracy of some of the miners, who were not going to be dictated to, bullied or beaten back onto the picket lines, without first having been given a national vote, as required by Union Rule 43.

Although the union at national level refused to give the miners a vote, the Nottinghamshire NUM decided to hold a district ballot. The results were that 7,285 members voted *for* strike action and 20,188 members voted *against* strike action. So, the miners obeying the area's democratic decision to work were unintentionally supporting the Thatcherite government.

Scargill, no stranger to the value of perception, began directing the blame onto those very same working miners, labelling them 'scabs', and turning miner against miner, as the issue became less about pit closures, economics and the loss of community, and more about making excuses for his dogged determination to bring the government down.

The strike also became hijacked by outsiders, extreme left-wing organisations that distributed propaganda within mining communities, fuelling an already explosive political situation. But this was not an issue for those outwith the industry, it was a war of attrition being fought by ordinary working people, who by now were just the meat in the sandwich, all incidental to the power struggle taking place between two sides unwilling to sit down and negotiate.

'So why did Vernon have such a sea change?' I asked, reverting back to my original point.

'Well,' she said, 'after Frank died, an' Scargill buggered off, that were it for Vern. He got totally disillusioned. Dint understand what he'd been fighting for all that time out on strike, wi Scargill refusing to negotiate but still happy to take his grace and favour. So, I suppose he rebelled and decided to gu tut UDM instead. He said they dint hold it against him that he'd been NUM or owt like that, an' membership were cheaper.'

She gazed through the kitchen window at the tiny flock of birds now feeding on the scraps of bread and pizza she'd left out earlier that day. 'All them years, Clare; stupid really.'

She looked at me and tried to raise a smile. She was intelligent enough to know that Vernon was dying and their time would now be short. 'Ah well,' she said, taking off the Marigolds and hanging them on the taps. 'No regrets; people like us just can't afford 'em.'

And I knew she wasn't talking about the brothers.

The Small Print Taketh Away

One day while I was studying roadways and drivages from the old mining plans laid out on the conference room floor, evangelical fridge magnet the Bounce came a bursting through the door.

'Clare!' she breathed, like she was offering me sex. 'Can you come down to Mr Stevens' office? And immediately, please. He said it's important.'

At the point of being 'Bounced' I was assisting in a research project funded by the UDM in order to establish whether miners had suffered knee injuries as a direct result of working underground. We had commissioned scientists from the University of Birmingham to carry out the epidemiology, and I was working long, hard hours vetting a sample of cases selected to take forward as tests for any subsequent litigation.

I stuck a yellow Post-it on a roadway in 53's main drivage, where one of my knee-injury claimants had worked, which was restricted to three feet in height and four feet in width. I wrote his name and check on the Post-it, pinning it securely to the site plan before rising to my feet.

'Blimey,' I winced, 'might have to bang a claim in mi self – what d'you think?'

'What do I think?' sighed she, patronising and not quite getting the joke. 'I think I'll definitely have to pray for you tonight.'

'Really?' I smirked. 'And will that be VAT-inclusive?' She never went out unless it was for a fee, and ran the bloody church for a profit. I honestly did want to knock her supercilious face off her born-again head with my patent-pink two-fifty-five classic. She was really going into overdrive with this Christian thing she had going on, which I found quite odd given that she was the most uncharitable person I'd ever met in my life.

Seriously, she'd become so decoupled from reality that she thought she knew God personally, and in another moment of startling enlightenment had actually told me that my friend Brian, (quite possibly the nicest man in the world) would definitely not go to heaven when *he* died.

'You have to go to church to be a Christian,' she'd spat, ' and you can't possibly be a Christian if you're gay!' Which of course was total twatology, because Brian was both.

Religion is never good when it's used in a false way, and the Bounce was one such person: she used her religion to make her feel superior to others and to show-boat the righteous. There was something inauthentic about her; I wasn't buying it, and so any contact we did have always had a whiff of the awkward about it.

That said, the Bounce wasn't the only person testing my ardour that day. Mick had become a lot more tyrannical in recent years, approaching even the most inconsequential of issues like a five-star general about to invade a small country. He suffered extremes of mood and, after a bout of rage, would shut himself down, stonewall you, then some time later, gripped by guilt, buy you some mad present, too inarticulate to even apologise.

'I dunt gee a fat rat's arse about your bloody partners! It's claimants that's our concern. What? Well, she's bloody well here now, Ken. Hang on, let me bleedin well explain to Clare what's bin goin on.'

I opened the door to his topsy-turvy office and, feeling slightly sick, sat myself down in a grim anticipation of the impending bun fight.

'Right, Clare, I've got Ken on. Now, hang on, Ken! Just a bloody minute!' He was looking at me, but screaming at Ken, who'd obviously asked to go on speakerphone.

'How'd the bleedin heck ...?' He was pressing buttons, not sure which was the speaker. 'This bloody phone. I'll be deploying bloody missiles in outa bloody space wi this bleedin thing!' (See genius.)

I stood up, pressed 'Conference', took the receiver from his hand and, after detangling the wire, placed it down quietly, in order that we could discuss whatever crisis had befallen us.

The phone call was about the misunderstanding surrounding solicitors charging rates and conditional fee agreements, which had caused Mick to become 'stuck in Dickie's meadow', as he put it.

The UDM had strict rules regarding solicitors charging claimants. The UDM, like all unions, charged a union membership fee but did not allow panel firms to charge the claimants, or to take money from

179

claimants' damages by way of success fees. Mick had assumed that a Conditional Fee Agreement was the same as a Success Fee (it wasn't) and had hit the roof. Ken was attempting to calm him down, when I'd walked in.

'Right, well, I've got another bloody letter about it, Ken, an' I want you tu sort it out, mek it right wit claimant, explain it in proper terms. Not in ten-page letters they can't bloody well understand, or am gonna hav tu tek all union's claims back!' This was always Mick's trump card, and by now most firms had become immune, but not Ken – he was a slave to the claim. Mick knew it, and played him well.

***

Uncle Ken was an ocean-going mammal, who'd been trawling the seabed of litigation for many a year. He was a push and shove, swallow a nail, shit a corkscrew type of lawyer: loud and obnoxious, with a bloated sense of self.

My Uncle-Ken-encounter of the very first kind came when I'd called his office to bollock him about contacting UDM claimants, who were becoming more than slightly irritated by his own particular brand of guerrilla marketing.

After taking a good twenty minutes of my gold-plated temper, he'd asked if he could visit the union with one of his senior partners in an attempt to get his firm on the UDM panel: a move that only a card-carrying, work-obsessed lunatic like myself could appreciate.

On arriving at the UDM, Ken was impressed, not just by our systems – which were modern, organised and efficient – but by the numbers. By now the UDM was a significant player and, being all about the money, Ken wanted the same level of success for himself.

Needless to say, as soon as he'd won his place on the panel, he was never going to settle for just a place on the panel.

'Come and work for me,' he'd pushed, in full poach mode, 'and I'll make you the "It girl" of the legal profession.' He wasn't looking at me, but at my bright orange Birkin, sitting as it was on its very own chair, commanding the room in soft luxury leather.

Now, don't get me wrong, even I could see there were elements of the ridiculous about someone prepared to wait for years on end just to get onto a waiting list in order to buy a handbag that cost almost as much as a second-hand car. But then again, just like every other full-throated, indignant bastard, he appeared to be missing one crucial point. *This*, was never about the money. And, while I admired his business acumen, I wasn't about to leave the union high and dry, nor was I going from frying pan into a legally binding deep-fat fryer, hog-tied in some exclusive agreement with Uncle Ken, the Arthur Daley of the personal injury circuit. No, they'd put their trust in me, the miners, and it was my absolute mission to deliver. I'd secured millions and millions of pounds in compensation on their behalf, and they in turn had put me exactly where I wanted to be: on top of my shit without even having to underplay my hair.

And, as he flounced his way out, it did cross my mind that only the most ridiculous money-eyed nincompoop, would ever underestimate a girl and her handbag; one might be made from the softest of skin, but the other, of course, was completely armour-plated.

Which, looking back now, was not only just as well, but incredibly clairvoyant, given the ferocious political fallout now set to ensue.

***

The closing date in respect of the Handling Agreements had allowed the DTI to finally focus on the exact numbers of claims being brought under each, and the figures in relation to the chest disease scheme did not sit easy with them.

The medical-assessment process for both living and posthumous cases was proving costly in many respects. Additionally, as priority had been given to the most elderly and severely disabled miners, the DTI were finding that most of the run-off cases were for those miners who might not be so severely disabled but still had to undergo a medical assessment that, in many cases, cost more than the claim itself. Therefore, they decided to go back to the trial judge and request a truncated medical assessment for those miners who had made a claim, but from their breathing-test results appeared not to be so seriously affected.

This form of allowing the claimant to opt out of the scheme would save the government millions of pounds in respect of medical fees and, ultimately, solicitors' costs. After all, if the miner opted out of the scheme at the breathing-test stage, rather than going to the second stage of a full medical, then the fee due to lawyers would be reduced, as the time each lawyer needed to spend in handling the claim was reduced.

This, I suppose, made sense to the DTI, but not to the lawyers like Uncle Ken, who'd invested time and money in new systems, taken on more and more staff and, like most businesses, carried out their future projections based on handling fees set out within the terms and conditions of the contract – the Claims Handling Agreement.

I'd also worked through the costing process with the UDM legal team and, although we were charging much less than solicitors, our costs would need to be ruled upon too.

It must be borne in mind that the DTI were after a significant, albeit unrealistic, reduction in costs, and were prepared to go to any lengths to achieve it.

In my experience, integrity is rarely found in the average government official, who can see everybody's point but their own, and would spin their own granny for a headline, so I don't know why I was so surprised by their next move.

***

At four o'clock one morning in June, my mobile flickered into life, with the familiar squeak of a message received. It hadn't really woken me. I was already awake, having been reeling from a difficult day, which had started with the Bounce marching into my office with a self-satisfied look on her face while placing copies of parliamentary questions onto my desk: questions being asked in the House by a 'serial killers are people too' backbench MP, regarding the UDM and its 'relationship' with the DTI.

I'd also taken a call that day from a colleague, who'd told me that rumours had been circulating that the union had sacked me. Not a concern in itself, you understand: lawyers are, by nature, more scavenger than hunter and can be worse than hairdressers when it comes to gossip.

No, the thing that set this *rumour* apart was that it appeared to have been part and parcel of the very same government whispering campaign.

'Well,' I'd spat, 'there are two major impediments to that little vignette: firstly, you're calling me at the union, so obviously, I haven't been sacked; and secondly, in my experience, most politicians appear to have a casual relationship with the truth and are inclined to hypocrisy, especially when it comes to money!' Slamming down the phone with an *'Idiot!'*

So, my already tweaked terror antenna was now sent into overdrive by the early-morning text. I couldn't leave it. I got out of bed went down to the kitchen, and put the kettle on. 'Coffee first,' I mumbled, letting out the cat. 'Can't function without caffeine.'

The message was from Uncle Ken. He, too, had heard that the union had sacked me for fraud and money laundering – nonsense, of course, but was I alright?

'What?' I cried, spitting out a wasp's nest. 'Money laundering? What does that even mean? I'm not the bloody godfather!'

I responded with a text full of '?????!!!', quite unable to control my temper. 'How dare they!' Still muttering out loud. 'How bloody well dare they!' I wanted to get in the car, drive to London and punch every single one of them in their supercilious, low-balling gobs, but after a four-shot espresso had thought better of it, opting for an early shower and a day in the office instead.

I was glad to get to the office that morning; it was 5.45 a.m. and I wanted to check my emails, read the latest paper for costs from Brian the Barrister, and breathe the air. This was important: breathing the air, taking in the atmosphere. I could usually smell trouble, and this had the whiff of a nappy fire. Something was wrong, so wrong I could almost touch it. The DTI, the whispering, the parliamentary questions … Why pick on a union?

I sat for a while, reviewing the minutiae. I knew where the rumour had begun, but not why. So I worked backwards: fraud, costs, lawyers, miners, money, government, contracts, politicians, government, lawyers, contracts, claims, money, money … money.

And just then, like a twat in the titter valve, all came clear.

With over 750,000 miners making a claim, the cost of both schemes had completely spiralled out of control, costing billions and billions of pounds in taxpayers' money. Not only that, but criticisms were now being made about government spending – their costs, their lawyers and their service providers – along with their inaccurate forecasts and final projections of the number of miners now eligible to claim.

They needed a scapegoat, a sacrificial lamb: something or someone to deflect the blame, highlight the money, create a resentment and sway the public into a gravy train scenario.

And in that moment, that perfect moment in time, the union was it: the perfect victim of choice.

After all, who would care if the strike-breaking union got a kicking? They had no real supporters in this particular government – the other two mining unions wouldn't mind the sport either and, who knows, it might even be payback. Plus, UDM claims were being headed by a woman: a woman who actually looked like a woman; a feminine woman in a position of power, not a fat, balding, Oxbridge twat with a Hanoverian underbite, dog-dirt breath and chronic gout. No, the contrast between dying miners, and their cash-rich union with its one-dimensional, handbag-toting Barbie Doll was just too much good copy.

Now they were out to get me, and not for anything I'd done, but for who I was.

I sat waiting for my computer to compute as I considered my next move.

We needed a lawyer, a swinging-sledgehammer, hard-as-nails, you-call-on-my-shit-and-I'll-call-on-yours type of lawyer: someone to dig us a trench, a big mother-fucking trench between the UDM and the storm of shit now making its way from Victoria Street to Berry Hill Lane. So I searched online to find the us the best, and up one popped, in the nick of time.

***

A week later, I was due to be in Leeds for one of a series of court hearings regarding knee injuries. The solicitors representing the other two miners' unions had started to become involved with the knee-injury

184

litigation. However, mistrust existed on all sides, and so a hearing was being held in order that all parties could register their interest and come together in a group action, regardless of union affiliation. A bit like a judge banging the heads of children together in the playground.

Over the years, attending review hearings had always been difficult: once Mick and I had been identified as UDM, we were social herpes. No one sat within spitting distance. Even when the court had been full to bursting, there was always a huge chasm between us and them, as if sitting near us would in some way render them scab-by-osmosis.

Today, however, the bullying was much more intense and not half as casual as before.

The whispering, sniggering and name-calling from people who were supposed to be 'professional' and, dare I say it, over the age of five, was quite breathtaking. Still, I refused to be cowed by a whinge of middle-aged lawyers acting like a bunch of twelve-year-old girls in training bras. I'd never wanted to be part of their 'walk the same, talk the same' gang, and, in any event, I was more concerned by the bruises I'd sustained from the pap chase outside my house the night before, and what it all meant.

Unfortunately, I didn't have to wait too long to find out. The pin had been pulled, and the brain grenade was on its way.

Chafing the Nappy Fire

It was 3.00 a.m., the very next day, when the telephone in my home office started to ring. In a torpid state I staggered to its call, but my bum-fuzzled bedhead was way too slow and, needless to say, I missed it by a mile. Then suddenly, my mobile – which was next to the bed – lit up its tinny chant, so off I wobbled, still half-asleep, tripping over anything that got in the way, finally scrambling for a grasp, before it, too, rang off.

It was Peter, a UDM lawyer. He was in London covering the hearing on costs. 'Clare! It's Peter.' His voice startled me. I was AWAKE now.

'Yes, yes, what's the matter? What's happened?'

'You're all over the early editions of the national papers! It's front page and goes on and on into the centre: page four, page five … it's hideous!'

'Front page as in the front page, front page? Why, what've I …?' I started to feel half-sick. I'd had a phone call from my lawyer the night before, who'd told me that the papers were going to do an article about me and the union, and that I should refrain from comment wherever possible. She said the pack was on the hunt, and because I had a vagina, big hair and an impressive collection of Louboutins the story had legs and was now set to run.

I, on the other hand, had completely failed to grasp the situation – it's hard to give in to such fantastical nonsense, especially when you're steeped in real life, so hearing Peter confirm the rumour was a bit like being in a fourth dimension – nothing made sense.

'But I don't understand … there's nothing to know.'

'You need to read it. It's got DT-fucking-I written all over it. We're in court today to argue costs, what a fucking coincidence! Bastards! I'd laugh if it wasn't so fucking crucial!'

How very odd to hear Peter swear: he'd always been so polite, so matter of fact and in control. This must have really pushed his button, the potty-mouthed one, that is.

'Okay, I'll get myself over to the union and sort it out. Can you call me when you get to court?'

'Yes, but I doubt the hearing will go ahead now. I really don't think the judge can ignore *this.*' He sounded tired and deflated.

'I'm so sorry, I don't know what to say.' I immediately felt guilty. The legal team had worked long and hard on the changes to the scheme, and then there was the issue of the knee-injury litigation. Any bad publicity could destroy all we'd worked so hard to achieve.

'Just don't let them give you a kicking.' His voice was breaking up. 'And don't speak to anyone you don't trust. On second thoughts, Clare … don't speak to anyone.'

I went downstairs, made some coffee, then into my office to get online and read the early editions. I knew I had to face it – whatever 'it' was – and, completely petrified, sat down, logged on and started to read.

The picture on the front page was, as Peter had said, hideous.

There was this woman, who'd not only ripped the government off in a seven-billion-pound fraud, but had also killed loads of sick and elderly miners, stolen their money and used the proceeds to buy some very expensive-looking handbags – I looked again, and saw that the woman was me.

Gulp, gulp, and thrice gulp. This was far, far worse than anything I could possibly have imagined. Pouring the coffee, I'd actually reached a state of calm, relieved almost that whatever 'they' were alluding to would be out there. I'd meet their allegations head on, fight back, clear up the misunderstanding and move on. But this was totally off the Richter. There was even a number, inviting anyone with shit to sling to get in the queue and start the freephone hurling.

I stared open-mouthed, in complete and utter gobsmackery, then, taking pen to paper, attempted a bullet-pointed list of allegations:

Clare Walker is the woman behind a seven-billion-pound fraud.

Clare Walker hoodwinked the Public Accounts Committee, five government ministers, thirty government officials and a battery of government lawyers.

Clare Walker buys handbags, doesn't work very hard, but for some mad reason gets paid a shitload of money.

And as a result, the Law Society has launched an investigation.

Not only that, but Clare Walker lives in a house like this and drives a car like that. So now, the flipping Serious Fraud Squad, South Yorkshire Police and the Serious Organised Crime Agency have decided to get into the ring.

But don't just take our word for it, people, look at this picture: Clare Walker is a doll's head!

And there it was – my list; an appropriate blend of spite and crap. I may not have spoken their language, but trust me, now I could hear every word they were saying. They were entitled to their own opinions, but not their own bloody facts. I may have committed the odd crime against fashion, but other than that, the press could go fuck themselves … or so I thought.

***

Escaping the house had proven difficult. The paparazzi had every exit covered, so I got to Berry Hill later than I'd intended that day.

Taking a deep breath, I got out of my car and, feeling more than slightly sordid, made my way across the car park.

A gaggle of flat caps and raincoats were on the approach, armed with copies of that day's news. At the vanguard was Mr Dunnicliffe, one of my very first claimants. Although his claim had been settled many years previously, Harry Dunnicliffe still popped into the union now and then for tea, biscuits and a trot down memory lane. Harry was a gentleman, but retirement had hit him hard and, like most of the old miners he missed the pit, the atmosphere of work and the camaraderie of old friends, some of whom marched with him now, as he led the advance.

'Nythen, duck, how's tha doin?' His voice was soft and warm.

'I'm sorry,' I wobbled. 'I don't know what it's all about.'

'Don't talk so chuffin soft, thas nowt to be sorry on. Y'can't kid a kidder, kidder, an' we're not as daft or as green as we're bloody cabbage lookin! But I will tell thee this for nowt …' he waved the paper to a point, 'if they're havin a gu at you, they're havin a gu at us all.'

He ran it along the line of men standing faithfully behind him, including Mr Tattersall, sitting defiantly in his wheelchair, complete with oxygen (tank and mask).

'D'you want us to walk y'in?' enquired Mr Fogg, from centre back. 'We've got flasks an' sandwiches. We can stop all bloody week if necessary.'

I gave them a long look, trying hard to raise a smile. 'That's really kind, but I think I'm going to have to face this one on my own.'

'An' if we know owt about thee,' snarled Harry, 'we're sure tha bloody well can. But tha not on thee own, an' there's nowt they can sai, or nowt they can do, that'll ever change that one, lass.'

'Thank you, that means everything to me.'

'Nowt to thank. Na gerrin theer an' sort um out. We'll watch you gu … gu on!' he ordered.

I pulled his hand to my mouth and gave it a grateful kiss, then, sick with worry, continued my way into the office.

By now it was clear that someone had been passing information to the press, and that nasty little trail of cat sick disguised as a bench MP, who, by the very nature of his job, was so well networked that he'd managed to sling just as much shit against the union as his parliamentary privilege would allow. There'd been quotes taken and leaked from minutes of UDM meetings; company documents taken completely out of context, twisted and spun.

The press had far too much detail of my day-to-day whereabouts, the venues I'd been asked to attend but cancelled at the last minute, the time I was leaving the office, the time I was arriving home, details of friends, their numbers, and messages I'd left. I'd deal with it once I'd identified the source, but for now, I needed to deal with the list, pick off each allegation, get the reality not the innuendo, hit it hard and stare it down.

Walking down the corridor, I passed the pictures of mining scenes past and present, the hand-filling, drivages and roadways depicting tell tales and doscos, all painted by an ex-miner the union had supported after he'd been incapacity-retired as a result of an accident at Thoresby pit.

I could hear my phone ringing off the receiver, so I picked up the pace, marched into my office and caught it before the answerphone kicked in. 'Hello, Clare Walker.'

Silence.

'Hello?'

A pause, and then, 'Hello, Clare. It's Jayne Naylor.'

Jayne Naylor was a square-in-shape, granite-faced she-mullet; a senior civil servant with a sniper for a tongue. She was clever, sharp and shrewd, but her unsparing determination to push difficult and vexatious issues through the framework of the scheme had always left us brawling, all the way to court. Peddling policies that were unfair, unjust and inequitable, she'd been forced to back down on many occasions. In fact, I'd recently given her a monumental battering over the strike-year debate, winning an extra year of exposure for those sick and elderly miners who'd worked during the strike – not a popular cause, but a worthy one. And now, sitting here in my office, I got the feeling there'd be a price to be paid for that kind of victory.

'May I speak to Neil Greatrex, please?' Her supercilious voice was set to put me in my place.

'Yes, certainly, Jayne, and how lovely to speak with you again. Hold the line, I'll just pop you through.' I actually wanted to pop her through the window, but stayed with the composure, in the vain hope that day may eventually come.

I put her through to Neil's office, and sat at my desk with my head in my hands. The red light indicating his line was busy taunted me for what seemed like a lifetime, and when at last it finally extinguished, I sat frozen to my chair until the door to my office opened up, and in marched Neil, with Mike McDonald, a UDM lawyer.

'Hey up, lass, tha looks dreadful.' Neil shook his head as he sat down, fag in hand.

'You don't look well at all, Clare. Are you up to talking through some issues or shall we leave you for a moment?' Mike was a gentleman, honest and straight. He and Peter were partners in the same firm and I trusted them both implicitly.

'No, no, it's alright. I haven't really slept. I was woken by Peter with the front page thing and … and … Sorry, carry on.' I was beginning to get on my own nerves, so I sat up straight and tried to raise a smile.

'Jayne Naylor from the DTI has stated that, in light of the

allegations in the press ...' Mike searched my face, looking for a softer delivery. 'The thing is, Clare, we all know what this is, but the minister has issued an ultimatum: unless you stand down from your position, he fully intends to withdraw both Handling Agreements from the UDM with immediate effect.'

And there we had it.

There it was.

And there I was, smacked back in time, back in that bed, with that old familiar feeling, clinging to my sister's nightdress, as I started to tremble and shake.

'Problem we've got,' Neil was back in the game, 'is vultures will be ont claims faster than a set on fuckers, and nobody wants that one, lass.'

His delivery was out, but he was bang on the money. If the DTI withdrew the Handling Agreements the already-panicked claimants would take their claims elsewhere and cases would haemorrhage from the union to ruthless lawyers, circling like a pack of famished hyenas round the carcass of the UDM. The staff would lose their jobs, the medical centres would close and the press would get a few more 'Clare Walker is a bastard' stories.

'You've got the best part of 20,000 cases left to settle, Clare. I don't have to tell you how much that would mean in the way of costs. Then there're all the policy issues that are specific to your claimants. You simply cannot let them withdraw the Handling Agreements. You can fight it. We could have them for breach of contract. But fighting takes time, and by then they'd be no claimants left to fight for.' Mike was right – he was always right.

'I know,' I whispered.

I suppose I should have been crying. I really wanted to cry, but the pain, deep and searing, had completely surpassed crying level. Besides, I needed to think, do the right thing by the claimants and the staff, which wasn't necessarily the best thing for me.

'I ... I've got some really nice claimants with difficult claims. They're very poorly, I don't want them worrying.'

I looked at Neil and he nodded his agreement. 'Jayne Naylor

wants me tu run things an' you tu step down. We've got tu call her back int next five minutes or them fuckers are gonna announce withdrawal of agreements tut press. I know it's hard, mate, but we've got no fuckin choice.'

I couldn't focus. The trembling was getting worse. I knew Neil was saying something, but his lips were totally out of sync with his words. Why was he talking so fast, but moving so slow?

'Clare … Clare? I'm getting more than worried.' Now Mike was doing it. 'You're shaking, come with me and I'll take you home.'

'No! No, I'm … I'm alright. Okay,' I wobbled, 'tell them – the DTI – tell them I'll stand down. But let me speak to my claims team first.'

'Alreight,' said Neil. 'Gerrum assembled int EC room, an' I'll phone Jayne Naylor and let her know.'

And in that moment, I was out, and everything I'd worked so hard to achieve completely snatched away. Not because I'd fucked up or done anything wrong, but because I'd been named and shamed in a twenty-four-hour trial by media. Accused of something I had not done, a crime I most certainly had not committed, by a set of snivelling bastards, incapable of taking responsibility for themselves or the government they represented.

I'd grown up with the schemes, both of them. I knew every schedule, sub- paragraph, comma and colon, exactly which of the 300 or so side letters attached to which policy issue, and every step of the medical-assessment processes in minute detail. I'd even put myself through a medical examination at Glenfield Hospital, so that I could properly understand how the miners felt and how the process worked. In the embryonic days of the COPD scheme I'd manually calculated underground dust readings taken from old pit records and X-ray data, before the dust calculator had even been invented. I knew each and every co-morbid issue and its impact on each disease. I could give respiratory specialists lessons in co-morbid fractions and lecture the impact of dual pathologies to vascular surgeons.

Minister after minister, civil servant after civil servant would come and go, and I'd seen them all. I was the constant, they were always the variable, and now they wanted me out.

This was nothing to do with fraud, charging miners or duping the Public Accounts Committee: this was a government spinning the shit onto the union to deflect from their own shortcomings, get a victory on costs, and yes, of course, stop the knee-injury litigation dead in its tracks. I should have seen it coming, but I hadn't, and now it was all too late.

I went back to my office and packed all my 'things': the little pink plant from Evelynne's room, and her photograph that had always resided on my desk; some books on mining and law; and the lucky piece of coal I'd got from Calverton pit, the day they closed it down.

Another life, in another box: a box I labelled 'Loveliness'; before making my exit, (via the back door of course), never to return.

***

The next few days were some of the most difficult I've ever had the misfortune to experience. The press attention terrified me, mainly because I didn't understand it.

And as the campaign grew, the articles became more and more vicious. TV crews arrived, TV crews left. I was on the early evening news, so I switched it off, closed the curtains, and went upstairs.

Avoiding anything to do with miners, fraud or handbags, I waited until night time fell, then packed a case and drove to London, arriving in the early hours of the morning.

I attended a meeting with my newly formed legal team, but had trembled and twitched so uncontrollably that they insisted I returned home and saw a doctor. I was present but not there. Now everyone was doing the fast-talking, slow-moving routine, even my GP. I tried hard to concentrate, but the overwhelming sense of impending doom, and the feeling that my life was sliding completely out of view, had invaded me. I couldn't eat, I couldn't sleep; there was nowhere to go and no relief. I couldn't run from myself, unzip my skin or shed the feeling of sheer and utter hopelessness. I trembled, I shook, I rocked back and forth, and for the very first time in my life, I actually wanted to die.

I was diagnosed as suffering from an acute adjustment disorder: a psychological disturbance that develops in response to stress. It occurs when an individual is unable to adjust or cope with a particular stressor –

in my case, the press, the accusations, luxuriant gossip and innuendo. My life was no longer going in an expected direction, the direction my brain had been programmed to accept, and so my brain, like the rest of my body, had lost its ability to function, and had shut itself down.

I was given a high dose of diazepam to flatten me, level me off, stop the trembling and hyper-anxiety. The doctor said that I should feel better almost immediately, and also gave me some antidepressants, which would take longer to kick in.

I was eternally grateful for the drugs: they allowed me to sleep and to function, without the trembling and twitching which, clearly, would have left me bumbling to disaster.

Survival of the Cutest

There's nothing quite like a raid by the Seriously Flawed Squad to set you up for the day.

I was raided at seven o'clock one July morning, approximately five weeks after being informed of the event by the national press, so I suppose the element of surprise had been lost to a certain extent.

Being raided by the police can, at times, be a very public affair. In my case, like so many others, the police turned up with a car full of journalists. I wasn't altogether sure how that worked – who phoned who, or if they'd managed a light pre-raid breakfast as a group first, in some barista-style coffee house, brainstorming round a bacon sandwich and a battering ram, or something like that. In any event, the police and the press arrived synchronised.

There was something about the heavy-duty door-banging that told me the Dibbles had landed. And so, through the milky film of Prozac, I calmly made my way downstairs, sporting a very attractive pink towelling dressing gown, and hair like forked lightning.

Finally opening the door to a small group of coppers, who, in bad Caramac-driven suits and Tie Rack neck garb were, to a man, the very definition of Rotherham.

'Clare Walker?' a balding chap with skin the colour of cheap soap bellowed from front of house.

'Yes,' I giggled – quite the wrong thing to do, but he looked like a cross between Les Dawson and someone flatlining in a cardiac unit, and to me, that was funny.

'I'm Detective Inspector Blah de Blah and this is Detective Sergeant Blurdy Blur from the Economic Crime Unit. We have permission to search these premises. May we now enter?' He held out some sort of search warrant in his fat little fist – I didn't examine it, but ushered them through to the kitchen instead, where I was told they had reason to believe that a serious fraud had been committed against the DTI, and/or (but not quite sure) the Union of Democratic Mineworkers. They were here to search the premises and remove anything that they thought would assist with their enquiries.

The taller of the two smiled. I supposed he was the one identified as 'good cop' in the breakfast brainstorm and, nose hair aside, was by far the most attractive of the gaggle.

'Don't worry, luv,' he soothed, 'we're not going to arrest you.'

I looked down at my dressing gown. 'I know it's a bad shade of pink and a bit nannan's knickers, but that doesn't make it a crime, does it?'

No one saw the funny side.

'Can you show us where the office is?' snapped Long Shanks, no longer smiling.

Right, now I was courting a spit hood and a Taser. This really was no time for levity, so I decided to back-pedal with a 'Is it okay if I just get dressed first?' instead.

'Well, we're supposed to keep you in sight,' bald Dibble butts in, 'but we'll let it go on this occasion, just as long as you're quick.'

I scuttled to the bedroom and slung on some clothes as fast as my bedhead would allow, returning to the kitchen with a completely different tack.

'Okay. Anyone want a coffee, while they're … er … raiding?' My words fading with the question.

'Yes, please, that'll be great,' chirped a fair-skinned bloke in a nylon shirt and shortened trousers, stroking the kitchen cupboards. 'Nice house,' he said, accusingly.

Yeah, and I bet you're gonna huff and puff till you blow it all down.

Just at that moment, more police arrived. A tall mad-eyed female, with a bristly top lip, and a head in the lower percentile, two other male officers and a bloke with a video camera, who wouldn't have looked too out of place shovelling chips at Greasy Vera's. And as the kettle simmered to its boil, I imagined the contents of my knicker drawer being strewn all across the bedroom floor in their hunt for the miners' millions.

***

Fear of the unknown appeared to have been the trigger for my breakdown, and the 'Clare Walker Murders Miners' storyline, the stressor. Now that the impending 'raid' had finally been completed, I felt the fog of fear lift. I'd been sleeping, but now, for some mad post-raid reason, I was *wide awake*.

It was no good fretting about prison, bankruptcy or sleeping in my car outside Dorothy Perkins on Rotherham high street. I needed to stop wallowing in all this insignificant victim crap, pull on the 'Girls Kick Ass' T-shirt and start my defence.

First up, I needed to get off the antidepressants. So I made an appointment to see my GP, who was happy to stop the diazepam immediately. I'd dropped the dosage over the last couple of weeks, and so could do without them now.

'You're going to have to continue with the Prozac, though, Clare.' His pleased face smiling at the more stable, wobble-free me. 'I can certainly lower the dose, but to stop immediately would give you withdrawal side effects.' He paused and, turning back to his screen, asked, 'Do you take any exercise?'

'Yes, always, before things went curly at work, and "back-stabbers" became my original soundtrack, that is,' I said, assuming he'd kept abreast of the 'Clare Walker Eats Kitten sandwiches' stuff, and of course he hadn't, so I continued. 'I used to exercise most days. I like to run. It's got me through some of the worst times: my divorce, losing my home, and when my dad … when my dad …' I could feel the tears beginning to well. Why now? Half-puzzled and half-pissed-off at myself. 'And, erm, when my dad … died.' I looked out of the window in an attempt to avoid eye contact. It was true, I'd been so disabled by all the fraud fright, that I hadn't even had the ability to exercise. Exercise had always been my cure, and how strange for this latest kick in the teeth to have affected me so, when there had been moments in my life that had been much scarier, much more painful. Seriously, why had I allowed something so ridiculous to send me over the edge?

Maybe, just maybe, I'd put unresolved issues into psychological boxes way too many times, compartmentalising, leaving them for another day. That day having now dawned, and Fraud Gate just a catalyst for igniting the pain still bubbling under the surface.

'Well,' said the doctor, 'exercise is a feel-good drug. If taken correctly, it stimulates serotonin, the feel-good hormone, and lifts your mood.' He tapped out a new prescription, tore it from the printer, signed it and, finally handing it to me, continued: 'This is a new prescription for a milder antidepressant. Take it in place of the old one and try to introduce some exercise into your daily routine. Come back in a month's time, sooner if you start to feel anxious, and we'll take it from there.'

***

I didn't transact the note. Like the remaining Prozac, it went into the bin. I wrote my own prescription that day: a large dose of Motorhead, mixed and mashed in equal measure with Her Majesty, the Mistress of Mindfulness, Madonna, a nip of Gangsta and a smattering of Punk. My banging battle-beat for beasting a 10K run in 2lb hand weights and a home-made face bra (prison or no prison, I wasn't going down with jowls), followed by an hour of hardcore weight training, on a regime that would burst the blood vessel of your left eye under any kind of normal circumstance.

But there was nothing normal or circumstantial about this. I was a collateral target, I needed to move fast, stay in my lane and focus on the win.

Research had told me that the average investigation by the Serious Fraud Office tended to span years not months, and that I should treat my investigation like a marathon, not a sprint. So, I trained like an endurance athlete in the mornings, and worked forensically on my case in the afternoons.

I bought boxes of lever arch files, one for every year I'd worked at the union, and stripped everything back – back to the start. I'd had the sense to have kept everything: all letters in, all letters out, all diaries, each and every email (sent and received), along with every meeting or team brief I'd ever had. Each page was a day in my life, as minute by minute, hour by hour, day by day, week by week, month by month and year by year, I recreated my career, cross-referenced the evidence, tagged anything I thought would be important, and built my defence line by line.

My lawyer said that I was unusual in my method of discovery, and my somewhat 'obsessive' approach to record-keeping, in that people who commit fraud don't tend to keep records, because fraud, by its very nature, is silent, covert and undercover.

Documents are not usually created, or if they are, they are soon destroyed. But evidence never forgets, and I'd always had the sense to keep my evidence: something that had been important to me when dealing with a government that could, and usually would, change the dynamic and rewrite the script at will.

My friends, family, union staff and officials were summoned down to London and questioned by the Serious Fraud Office over and over again, along with every solicitor, barrister, accountant and tea lady that had ever crossed my path, as statements were taken, edited and rewritten with alarming regularity.

One union official was told, 'You will make a complaint against Clare Walker, or we'll arrest you.'

'You'd better arrest me, then,' he replied. 'I'm not making a complaint.'

Another union official was asked to sign a statement. After reading it with care he pushed it back to the copper sitting opposite. 'You sign it,' he said. 'It's your statement, not mine.'

This scattergun approach is also a much-practised modus operandi of your average politician, particularly when covering their own mistakes, and by now the government had set off so many investigations into the UDM that it was difficult to decide which one to fight first, as we became the target of every greedy lawyer and ruthless politician in the land.

But never to be oppressed, in this little union we did what we did best: we took them on, 'the triangle of love' (police, press and politicians), eating our elephant piece by piece, fighting and winning each and every action, to the Court of Appeal and back down again.

However, despite its victories, this proud, caring, well-meaning organisation had finally paid the price and, unlike its emblematic phoenix, never rose up from the ashes of its shattered reputation.

***

Sadly, the union's victory was not the end of the fight for me – I was still a person of interest. After the Fraud Squad had raided my home, they froze my all assets – including my bank accounts – retreated to London and tapped my phone. My reputation had been trashed, so much so that I was officially unemployable and, by now, borderline bankrupt.

So, when I was questioned some four and a half years later, I was more than desperate to finally clear my name.

I was the last to be interviewed in what appeared to be an arse-about-tit methodology of police work. There was no complainant and no apparent victim – I had, in fact, been investigated for a fraud that did not exist.

Further, I was not expected to present my side of the story, and was met by a barrage of incredulity from the Chief Staple-Puller, after turning up for interview with a seventy-four-page statement in my defence: a truthful, bulletproof account of my life, along with real and tangible evidence to verify each and every line. I was duly informed that my interview would have to be rearranged as a direct result of this 'unexpected' turn of events.

Really, thought I, *do the Dibbles seriously expect to lock me into a system I have no control over, destroy my career, reputation and mental health, put my life under the microscope, take evidence from everyone and anyone about what I may or may not have said, what I may or may not have done, drag me through the dirt, publicly humiliate me, threaten me with prison and bankruptcy, warn friends and family to stay away from me, keep me in a heightened state of stress for years on end, sitting on the sidelines like some sort of spectator to my own life whereby they dictate the process ... and expect me not to defend myself? Really?*

'We'll need to speak to your client in two weeks' time, once we've had time to digest the statement,' they told my lawyer, not even bothering to glance my way.

So we left, returning three weeks later when an actual interview took place.

Their questions, which were almost as offensive as their hairstyles, gave away much more than the answers they received. Was I dyslexic? Did I have sex with men to bolster my career? Had I ever called

Mick names? Did I tell lies? Was I stupid? Did I dupe the DTI, the Public Accounts Committee and four government ministers? Or did I just have sex with them? What about any of the miners? Did I have sex with any of them? And what about Cyril the UDM squirrel: what was the relationship there?

I sat in silence giving them a vacant stare, thinking, either I'm a master criminal of epic proportion, a genius trapped in a bimbo's body, or just a bimbo, willing to play hard and fast with her sexuality – they can't have it both ways! Additionally, and for the purposes of the tape, I hadn't realised that being dyslexic was a fucking crime!

And so, after three days of an insult-to-my-intelligence grilling by a set of dexterous monkeys in bad shoes, peddling poisoned coffee, soft biscuits and arrogant smirks, I was told that I would hear within the next three weeks as to whether I was going to be charged. Unfortunately that wasn't the case: I didn't hear from them for another year, during which time they interviewed everyone from the beginning again.

Love is the Lesson

Wednesday morning began like most others. I woke from an interrupted night's sleep, having no immediate recollection of the dark cloud still hanging over my head. But then, I opened my eyes, and there it was, bleaker than a hangman's gaze, that invisible prison of a constant worry.

The telephone rang, and I pulled the bedclothes over my head in the hope that it would stop when I blanked out the light. Eventually it did and, finally finding the strength to force the boulder of despair from my chest, I shuffled to the bathroom in old sheepskin slippers to draw my morning tub – a relatively new ritual, more calming than a shower, nowhere near as much energy required.

Taking off my dressing gown, I checked my look in the mirror, the slow-eyed stare, the roadkill hair and the small horizontal scar of a recent hysterectomy: an emergency resolution after the invasion of an evil gang of fibroids, just a few weeks before.

'Wombs are good for two things,' exclaimed my surgeon, through the lisp of a very pronounced overbite. 'Breeding children and breeding cancer.'

His tone hadn't caused me any offence. To be honest, I'd always had a very difficult relationship with my cervix, so in a way, goodbye to that had been a total relief in the end. No, it wasn't the whys and the wherefores, or the fact that I had a womb with murder on its mind that had finally left me struggling. It was the complete void of a nothingless woman its removal had left behind. That and the fact that no one ever thinks to warn you about all the flatlining.

Seriously, I'd been dead for weeks, and apart from a 'Don't do the hoovering', no one, and I mean no one, not even the medic with the mad malocclusion, had even thought to apprise me of the unbearable rigmarole and half-lit fatigue of a post-menopausal bum-fuzzled brain.

Then again, I thought, now testing the water with a toe, it was always going to be a toss-up which would arrive first: a Serious Fraud Squad reprieve, or the menopause. And of course, in the end, the menopause won. So for now, I'd take to the bubbles, in the hope of finally finding some Zen.

***

Forty minutes on and I got myself out, dried and dressed before plucking up the nerve to finally check my phone. The missed call had been from Mick. His deflated voice told me that the union had won the last of its court battles, having secured injunctions against the two employees who'd leaked confidential documents to the press and others during the early days of Desert Fraud.

See, this is why I dreaded the phone these days – nothing but sad, sad, news, from one call to the next, and the headaches and heartaches from the squeakers and squealers who'd pointed the finger before finally ridding themselves of the responsibility of me, had seriously left me with nothing to say.

'I don't know what I find more disappointing,' I mumbled, fastening the buttons of my bright red coat, 'the disloyalty or the stupidity.' And with that, left the house to meet my ex-husband for lunch.

Easter was just around the corner, so I made a strict mental note to get all egged-up on the way back home.

***

As his illness tightened its grip, Tony had moved back home to be nearer his family, and had settled back to life in Great Ayton, a tiny village just outside Middlesbrough.

I loved the north-east of England, and played my *Northwinds* CD at full blast as I drove at speed up the A19, towards the salt-and-pepper-pot skyline.

Parking up, I could see him on the approach, walking stick in hand, determined to greet. 'Hello, hun, looking dazzling, as usual.'

'Morning, comrade, how the hell are you?' I grabbed him tight, keeping the hold slightly longer than maybe I should.

'Yeah, great. Planning a post-lunch fell run up Roseberry Topping if you fancy it later?'

'You run it,' I winced, 'I'll watch!'

We linked arms and slowly made our way to the tiny village café, a frequent haunt, for cheese on toast and a cup of hot chocolate, taking our places at a table for two snuggled neatly into the corner.

Shuffling his chair to a tighter tuck, he slid me a look. 'So, Monica Poundcoin,' he said, 'still starring in Crimestoppers, I see. Only, I read some more stuff in the papers last week. It was raining, and I think they said it was all your fault.'

'That's right. So if I were you, I'd check that stock in Russian squirrel pelts, because apparently, the pound's just fallen two points behind the garbanzo bean. Again, all down to me and my elegant cross-body bagging.' I scanned the menu (although without need, it was always going to be cheese on toast). 'To be honest, I don't read it any more. I just wish they'd stop using that bloody picture. Y'know, the one that makes me look like Adrian Street, the Diana Dors of all-in wrestling, channelling some sort of an escaped lunatic.'

'That's why they use it!' He laughed, unzipping his fifteen-tog Mount Everest lagging jacket. 'Because you look ridiculous.'

'Indeed,' I smirked, with a nod to the Chris Bonnington. 'Ridiculous!'

'So, what do the lawyers say? Are you going to be alright?'

'Yep, apparently it's just a matter of time.'

'Ah, come on! How much bloody time do they need? How long's it been now? Thirty ... forty years? How long?'

'Five,' I mumbled.

'Five years! Five fucking years! What a complete waste of taxpayers' money, not to mention all the shit they've put you through! It's a disgrace, a bloody disgrace.'

'I know. I'm seriously thinking of writing a book.'

'Ha! Yeah, neither am I'

'Well, it's either that or a protest song and, according to popular culture, writing a book is a very good way of recycling all the rage.'

'Is it really?'

'Yes, look at Diana. And you never know, I might be the next Sylvia Plath, or Simone de Beauvoir, or someone like that—'

'D'you reckon?'

'— but obviously, not Barbara Cartland, because, let's face it, I am realistic.'

'Quite.'

We paused as the waitress took the order.

'No, but seriously, Clare – five years? Most prison sentences don't stretch to that.'

'That's just it, that's exactly how I feel. Like I've served the bloody sentence, but committed no crime ... unless you count being in possession of a really nice kitchen, of course.' I bouffed my hair. 'Don't get me wrong, I'm not for one minute glad it happened, but in a perverse sort of way I am quite grateful for the lesson. Does that sound mad?'

'No, it sounds like you're living in a fortune cookie. I don't know about Barbara Cartland, but move over Confucius, there's a new kid in town.'

'No, really, I've learnt so much.'

'Such as?' He wasn't buying it.

'Well, for a start, who my friends are. And I know you're gonna say that's a total cliché, but believe it or not, what I hadn't quite grasped right up until now, is that clichés are clichés for a reason, aren't they?'

'Well, yeah, but you've always been smart like that.'

'I have, but I never realised just how flaky some people can be. They believe everything they read in the bloody papers.'

'Not me, kid. I'm with the "where there's smoke there's usually *no* fire" brigade.'

'Just smoke signals?'

'Exactly.' He leant in. 'And all that criminal stuff ... just a gag?'

'Right again, professor. Once an investigation of the criminal kind has been set off, you're immediately ordered to make no comment, and totally prevented from defending yourself in any public arena, because anything you may say might be used against you and all that crap. So you say nothing, and I've said nothing for the last five years, which for a lip-trotting professional mouthpiece like me is a huge ask—'

'Indeed,' he interrupted, but I'd started, so I decided to finish.

'Then agen, I always knew it was gonna be me that took the hit. Well, me and this darn pelvis, that is ... Seriously, being "the accused" is like having a contagion: no one ever comes near. And to add insult to that manufactured mountain of injury, they keep printing the friggin lunatic picture ... Still, like I said, I'm grateful for the lesson.'

'Well, for what it's worth, I think it's outrageous. Five years stolen from any life is a very long time.'

I looked into his eyes. He was so poorly, so worn out, and yet still had more care and concern for my stupid, insignificant little problems which, let's face it, were never going to be as big as his own. 'Anyway,' I said, 'never mind all that bollocks. How are you? Really, how are you coping?'

'Well, that's why I wanted to see you.' He took a moment.

'The thing is, I haven't felt right for weeks.'

'Really? Like what?'

'Well, just stupid things at first, and to be honest, I thought it was the drugs that weren't right. So I made a few appointments, had a few tests, and now, it turns out that I'm probably not going to make it after all.'

Silence.

'Sorry?' I felt a lump in my throat.

'The cancer,' he whispered, 'it's terminal, and unfortunately, it's moving fast.'

'No, no, no, you can't just go giving in now,' I ordered. 'You've fought too hard. What d'you mean, "moving fast"? What do the doctors say?'

'Well, that's just it. They've removed as much of the tumour as possible, but they can't take it all. And apparently, it's just gonna keep coming back, an' I'm ... I'm not gonna make it, kid, and I wanted to tell you now, in case there was anything you wanted to say ... y'know, talk about, before ...'

Talk?

I couldn't.

I was stuck, stuck in a moment, a dreadful moment of piercing clarity. Of course there was a lot I wanted to say about the cruelty and unfairness of it all, and how he didn't deserve it. But that lump in my throat was getting bigger by the second and had rendered me speechless.

'I've had my dark times,' he said, looking up once more. 'I've panicked, I've cried, even drank myself into a coma trying to escape it. But there really is no way out. And I can't outrun it, I'm too exhausted.' He forced a smile. 'Besides, the walking stick's a bit of an impediment.'

I took his hand and we sat in silence, a silence broken only by the clatter of china cups and the muffled conversations of people around us.

I knew him well. The very last thing he wanted was to go through it all again and again.

Cancer, the cruellest disease, had slowly but surely taken everything away: his looks, his independence, his ability to drive, walk or write; his left side was paralysed and his speech impaired. He was sick and tired from all the operations, the chemo- and radiotherapy. The steroids bloated him, frustration angered him, the cancer fatigue flattened him, and now it was going to kill him. Yes, he was dying, but he wanted round it, not in it, and I had to respect that.

'You can count on me, you do know that, don't you? No matter what, you can always count on me.'

'I know, but it's … it's difficult.' Caught in his emotions, unable to continue and avoiding my eyes as the waitress brought the food. Now he was sinking. He needed a diversion, something to switch the subject and stop the bleed.

I sat silently in the shadow of fear for what seemed like an age, frantically searching for something to say, something to reassure, pull him out and ease him back to normality.

Then finally, in a complete blind and utter panic, I blurted, 'I brought you some more music.'

'Yeah?' he said, with a relieved smile.

'Yes, remember that album you used to have? The one that David Coverdale signed when you went to see him in 1970-something-or-other?'

'Er … yeah'

'Well, hook your thumbs back into your Farahs and hold on tight to the top of that mullet, because *Northwinds*, my friend, is back!'

'No! I'd almost forgot about that.' He looked down at his plate. 'Can you do the honours?'

'Course I can. Pass it over.' I cut his food into bite-sized pieces.

'And, I've also brought some Prefab Sprout, just in case you get desperate.'

'Wow, cheese on toast, David Coverdale and an emergency pack of Prefab Sprout. Does it ever get much better than that?'

'Well,' I said, pushing back the plate, 'as a matter of fact, it does.'

'Really?'

'Yes, you mad fool. It's Easter soon – Jesus-film season!'

'So it is. Right then, we'd better make sure we get all egged-up on the way back home.'

It is strange, but during our married life, and notwithstanding the extramarital hiccup, there hadn't been much domestic turbulence. In fact, the two most violent arguments Tony and I ever had were: 1. Mini Cheddars and the Seasonal Snack Issue; and 2. Jesus Films – The Criteria.

For me, anything with a Roman soldier, ancient Egypt and the odd charioteer probably qualified, whereas Tony was a purist and had a very concise list – *The Greatest Story Ever Told*, *The Robe*, *King of Kings* and *Ben-Hur* – insisting on an absolute adherence to the subject matter. For him, there had to be an actual appearance.

'I think you can include *Spartacus*,' he said now, 'but *Antony and Cleopatra*? That's not gonna cut it; wrong message completely – all citizens of Rome, not enough urns and *way* too many tribunes.'

'Really? Good sandal action, though.'

'Let's agree to disagree.'

'Alright, but what about the Mini Cheddars – more your glass of red in winter, than a glass of white in spring?'

'Tell you what, I'll have a little think, while you write a little book.'

***

After lunch we walked to the tiny flat that had been converted to accommodate his disabilities, and chatted late into the afternoon, playing our music, remembering happier times, avoiding anything to do with death or dying, until it was time for his nap and for me to go home.

No longer my husband, Tony was a dear, dear friend, and our relationship, although platonic, was always romantic, always close. I was grateful to have him in my life and, despite its imminent dawn, could never imagine a day when he wouldn't be there.

And in that moment the gift of perspective finally took hold.

I no longer feared prison, bankruptcy or shopping at Primark. I may have flatlined on oestrogen, but I hadn't flatlined full stop. Enough of the endless despair, throbbing eyelashes and chronic self-pity. Some things cut deeper, sting sharper and hurt more, much more, than pounds, shillings and pence. Of course, it's no coincidence that the number of *friends* I had appeared to have diminished at the same time as my bank balance but, as Evelynne would say, 'love is the lesson, money never taught us to learn', and the few I have left are trusted and loyal. They push the Clare Walker stock up – it is they who make me a rich girl.

Yes, perspective definitely took hold, and Thursday morning began like no other – not a cloud in sight.

***

With a family pack of Creme Eggs chilling nicely in the fridge, I was scanning the TV guide, contemplating the four ingredients for a successful rebirth – tea, Jesus film, Easter egg, sofa – and was bitterly disappointed to find wall-to-wall Harry Potter, but no significant portrayal of why we consume our own body weight in chocolate at this time of year … not a leper, tomb or commandment in sight.

'What's wrong with TV these days? Where's the sense of culture?' A direct question to the cat, who was oblivious to my rant, curled up tight on the front room curtain with his head in his paws.

At that moment my phone rang. It was my lawyer in London, the most serious man on the planet, who, in an unfamiliar – and, it has to be said, frighteningly chirpy – voice informed me that the Serious Fraud Office, along with the Serious and Organised Crime Agency, had decided to drop their investigation due to 'a significant lack of evidence', and that I would not be charged with any criminal offence.

My tears of relief were soon followed by an overwhelming sense of injustice. Five years of helping the police with their enquiries had turned me into a ground-standing, chin-turning, willing-to-be-quiet-until-it-was-time-to-speak, professional bun-fighter, on the front line of a battle that had taken much more than just muscles and balls.

So, who to speak to when you're feeling angrier than Alistair Darling's eyebrows? Who would prevent me from running a naked paintball round in the House of Commons? ... Who?

I needed air, and to escape the house that had been Team Fraud HQ for the last five years, and now had a whiff of *Within These Walls* about it.

I took my coat from the closet and put on my hat. Then, taking the direction of old Kiveton Pit slowly made my way down Colliery Lane. The altitude of freedom had inspired me to sprint, but the four-inch heels were a bit of an impediment, as finally I came to a stop, and sat myself down on a bench made for two.

The sound of the traffic and the noise of life were different today, softer somehow, and not half as oppressive as before. *Well,* thought I, almost cracking a smile. *This is class. I've finally turned into that woman from way back when, sat outside the Albion with the fake-fur trim – stabbed in the back, but still wearing my hat.*

I glanced at my watch, it was almost midday and by now the sun was sifting through the grey, so I adjusted the brim and settled back to my seat.

Two women were standing at the bus stop, their hair blowing wild as the wind picked up, falling flat as it quickly dropped. They were discussing the Nectar points and how best to spend them, with children in baby buggies calling for attention as the conversation ran along.

Across the street an old lady was bringing back the shopping in a green tartan two-wheeled trolley. She had a little girl with her, her granddaughter I presumed. They were holding hands and singing songs, like we did, Evelynne and I, on the way back from the market, and I wondered what she would have made of all this.

The precious lessons I'd learnt at my grandmother's knee had left me staying and fighting. Packing my heap and facing the giant – that cosy network of the arrogant and ambitious, and the nexus between their half-truths and lies. I knew she would see just how strong I stood today but, in

210

the end, I was glad she'd been saved all the worry.

I sat, watching life go on, the past rubbing with the present, my eyes now fixed on the old miners' wheel, a commemorative monument, with significant names etched out in its tribute, and recalled my old claimants, the miners, dying from crippling lung diseases as a result of the long hard shifts spent in getting coal. I was proud to have run against the crowd with them, herding yet again with what some may perceive as 'the wrong gang'.

At that moment, and as if by magic, a flat cap in a sports jacket suddenly appeared with a little black wire-haired terrier. 'Aye up,' he said, with an automatic smile.

They made a good pair, the old man and his dog, its little legs now eager to pick up the pace: like Granddad William and Kit. And as they crossed the road to continue their journey, my thoughts turned to that of my father. My father was a drunk and, like most drunks, nostalgically prone. I could hear his voice, he was saying: 'The more things change, the more they stay the same ... doll face'.

I looked back down the lane, and saw the familiar silhouette of my friend on the approach. Caroline, a true friend, had stuck by me when others had not. She was the one who rang when the phone had stopped ringing; the one who rescued me when the press had me held like a prisoner in my own home; the one who'd been ordered to break all contact with me, but had refused on the grounds of friendship and love.

I took off my hat, in an attempt to shield my eyes from the sunlight now blazing overhead, and waved her forward with a smile.

Envy Will Hurt Itself

Someone once said, that the things we most aspire to in life are also the things we most despise in others. Having had a somewhat 'necessitous' childhood myself meant that I'd never stopped aspiring.

For me, it wasn't about the perfect marriage or the trouble and strife of a perfect child. I never wanted to hit the nappy train, and after the last trip out, didn't particularly want a husband either. No, my aspirations were relatively low-key, in that they began and ended with a career.

I'd learnt the hard way that in life you just can't rely on anyone else. That people, by their very nature, will always let you down. And in the end, the mend is always up to you.

In this respect, my career had set me straight and gave me everything I needed: a bunkered independence, free from restraint or the ridiculous need for a constant permission. It wasn't about domination or money, even though I appeared to be in the Monica Poundcoin phase of my life. I had to dominate to survive – the money was the bonus, never the driver.

True, I had a few pairs of power towers, a designer wardrobe and more than a passing interest in handbags, but really, is that a crime? After all, I'd fought long and hard in the bearpit of claims and, quite frankly, felt I deserved the cache.

Men flash their Bentleys and designer clothes and everyone assumes they've worked hard for 'it'. The same does not apply to women. I wasn't born to money, I didn't marry it – I made it myself and that's empowering. Even so, I managed to inspire envy in others, who began to secretly resent my success and set out to extinguish it by creating a fiction of crime.

Envy is misguided; it dangles in despair, and to compare yourself with others is the fast track to unhappiness. Unhappiness is easy, because it involves giving in. But I was born in a city built on heavy industry and strong women, running with the wrong gang in a street where no one else could see my scars. So, if I'm going for a fight, I'll continue to dress for a party.

I am, after all, a salt-over-the-shoulder, superstitious kind of person. I believe that blue flames, like black cats and being shat on by pigeons, are symbolic of good luck.

True, I have been shat on, and not always by pigeons, but still, I know I'm lucky.

I saw a shooting star.